PINK ELEPHANTS

Escape from the Loony Bin

LLOYD NEGOESCU

First Printing: 2017
ISBN: 978-1-365-76125-6

Second Printing: 2023
ISBN: 978-1-64649-302-9 (print)
ISBN: 978-1-64649-303-6 (ebook)

www.lloydnegoescu@comcast.net

CONTENTS

A Message from the Author

Write after re-write made me aware that the only way to adequately convey my perception of this bizarre reality and its myriad of characters was to write in the third person. I am certain there are other perceptions, but to the best of my recollection, I ask that you accept mine.

—Lloyd

ONE

MRS. GIPE AND
THE MEDICAL MERRY-GO-ROUND

*"...No man is an island, entire of itself; every man is
a piece of the continent, a part of the main. Any
man's death diminishes me, because I am involved
in mankind; and therefore never send to know for
whom the bell tolls; it tolls for thee..."*

—John Donne, *from Meditation 17,*
Devotions Upon Emergent Occasions

Lloyd was angry on so many levels. It was February 1965, and leaving his family for his next impending admission to a hospital two and a half hours from home was not making him any happier. He was frightened over the possibility that the girl he had only been "exploring" at night would get pregnant. At 14, he didn't understand that in his condition, he was incapable of getting anyone pregnant. He was tired of constantly answering the same question, "What happened to you?" And tired that he answered the same way each time, "I was shot."

His thoughts of being "shot" were like ancient water-drip torture. *I was shot! I was shot! I was shot!* Each repeat reminded him that he had to be cool and show no emotion, while exploding with every internal intonation. Such thoughts cannot leave a mind unscathed.

The night before his admission, Lloyd spent like so many before. In bitter torment he cried himself to sleep. A broken heap of dislocated hips, a curved spine, bed sores and raging infections he whimpered, "Why me, Goddammit?"

Lloyd was no saint. Swearing was not foreign to him. He wasn't a cute kid by any measure. He had thin, straggly brown hair and his nose was long and narrow with a bulbous tip that nearly touched his chin. He was well into his acne stage. His face was a canvas of measle-pocked red spots. He was teased incessantly by other children, which brought nothing less than outright hostility from him, his voice being his greatest defense. The school bus driver, who often overheard him, had already warned him that he'd be put off the bus if *"...you don't watch your language!"*

Lloyd swore like his father, a hardened farmer turned businessman, but only to his contemporaries. He always turned on the charm to his elders, like a New England bookworm. "Yes, please," and "No, thank you." It was a bitter lesson learned painstakingly from his abusive older brother. He hated the routine, but was smart enough to show deference to those in control.

He was instructed by his stepmother Lila to only pack a small bag when he left home at 7:00 AM that bitter cold morning. With remnants of snow from a recent storm still on the ground, the drive was slow and arduous. Lila was as cold and distant as the landscape they passed. Lloyd had been a thorn in her side for far too long, and she was relieved the day had finally arrived for his admission to the Pennsylvania State Hospital for Crippled Children in Elizabethtown.

They were alone and as she drove, she droned on and on about how this move would benefit the entire family. With his repeated hospitalizations, she constantly accused Lloyd of draining the family on many levels, most especially financially.

"Lloyd, you know admitting you in this hospital will be better for you and us. Don't be sad. Chin-up! Show some maturity. Do as you're told, and don't give the nurses or doctors a hard time!"

Lila always considered herself a deeply religious woman. Being married to Lloyd's father, a handsome philanderer who cursed constantly, didn't show much evidence of that. She said her prayers kneeling bedside, and never missed Mass on Sunday. Something in the deepest recesses of Lloyd's brain kept reminding him that he had a much closer relationship with her when he was younger. That was his only consolation for the barrage of abuse she doled out on a daily basis.

Before the "accident," she'd taught him songs and taken him places. She was beautiful and vibrant back then, a model with great potential. She and Lloyd's father were living together in Allentown, Pennsylvania. That was before she discovered his father had four other children waiting for their father to return home to New Jersey.

Lloyd's father hadn't told Lila at the beginning of their relationship. He knew she was far too traditional to ever get involved with a married man. After she fell head over heels for him, and the existence of Lloyd's family was finally revealed, Lloyd's father convinced her he would never have to take custody of his four children. His father was wrong about that.

It was shortly before 9:00 AM when Lila and Lloyd finally arrived at the hospital's outer gate. The road leading to the institution wound through a thick forest with towering trees that spoke volumes about the age of the area. Though building access was clearly marked and the road well cared for, the lane of thick vegetation was evidence enough that this place and its inhabitants were meant to remain excluded. Its distance from home also informed Lloyd that he was being dispensed with in a manner unlike other hospital stays.

The road to the institution wound through a thick forest with towering trees.

Well within the deepest part of the woodland, the driveway opened up to a circular courtyard with what appeared to be a large fountain in the middle, overgrown with shrubs and weeds.

There was a row of sectioned apartments on a hill to the left, and the main building with its wide stone patio leading to an ornate entrance stood majestically to the right. Despite visible wear and its overgrown moss and mold, it was easy for Lloyd to assume that at one time this monstrous structure and its surrounding lush flora could have been someone's palatial estate. He learned later that in its early days it was used as an insane asylum.

Whoever designed it had creative ideas on how to treat the disabled. On either side of the central vestibule, the wings of the large gothic structure were lined with windows, high and low. With lights on, tall glass doors with their own balconies revealed metal beds and scurrying activity.

In its early days, the building was used as an insane asylum.

A male orderly motioned for them to follow a slippery path to a much smaller door down and away from the front entrance.

The orderly's rough-worn, short-sleeved, starched white shirt, white starched pants, black shoes and black belt revealed a strict discipline. Without speaking, he held the door open and gestured Lloyd and Lila to enter. He didn't appear the type to smile much, but was kindly, and although diminutive in stature, exuded great strength.

Once inside, he only communicated in gestures as he led them up an inclined, dark hallway to a landing and an old elevator at the opposite end. Lloyd and Lila felt as though they were entering a tomb.

Sweat dripped from exposed pipes overhead and puddles formed on each side of the narrow passage. It reminded Lloyd of other hospital basements he'd seen. At 4'9", hunched over and walking in a gangly four-point style, Lloyd was careful to keep his crutches perpendicular to the floor to avoid slipping on the moldy and uneven concrete.

The air was cool but dank and musky. Lloyd struggled to keep up. His gait was slow and awkward as he crept toward the heavy gray metal doors where Lila and the orderly were waiting. He could hear the clang of grinding gears as the man pushed the button on the wall to call the old conveyor box.

Lila whispered to the orderly, "He's really put me through the mill!"

The orderly only nodded. He had heard it all before. What bothered him was that family members always said things like that within earshot of their children.

After what may have seemed like endless moments to the man and Lila, the time it took the elevator to descend was ample for Lloyd to reach the landing. Just as he arrived, the box came to an abrupt stop. Its two outer doors opened to reveal a sunken floor where the box had not stopped flush, and large brass folding-latticed gate doors inside.

As though choreographed, the man uttered his first words to them. "Watch your step. The elevator never stops where it should."

Stepping down to enter the cab wasn't an easy task, but Lloyd received no help. He wasn't surprised that Lila remained distant, though he had expected some assistance from the orderly.

The elevator cab was badly beaten and very shaky. Scratched and dented from far too many years of service, it was hard to determine the original paint color.

The orderly pulled the latticed doors open and held the outer gray doors until Lloyd was planted against the back wall. Then, he slammed the brass doors shut and allowed the outer doors to close on their own. Once encased in the man-made tomb, the smell of urine seared Lloyd and Lila's nostrils. Overexposed, the orderly showed no sign of discomfort. Lila, however, recoiled in disgust.

The orderly lifted the ends of the latticed gate, placed the hook of each carefully in the slot, and pushed the button. Nothing happened. Then, he pulled the inside doors back and, slamming them a little harder this time, feverishly pushed the button. Still nothing.

Lila and Lloyd stood motionless, eyes forward, anxiously waiting for something to happen. Lila wanted to comment, but like Lloyd, was a captive audience.

The orderly cursed under his breath, pushing the button a few more times, but the cab refused to move. Lloyd was too scared to be amused, but watching Lila, took a modicum of pleasure at her disdain.

The orderly kept pushing the button as though varying intensities would make the frail wires connect. Giving up, he readjusted the folding metal gate again to be sure it locked. Once he was satisfied he had done all he could, he pushed the button for the first floor again. This time you could hear the current connection.

Crack!

Contact was made and they began their rickety ascent. Lila breathed a sigh of relief. After what seemed like an eternity of spits and starts, they reached the first floor.

When the elevator stopped, they were warned once again to watch their step. With the orderly holding the outer elevator doors open, Lila gingerly stepped out, then reluctantly, Lloyd.

What they encountered was a bizarre bee-like frenzy of activity. It was immediately evident that this was the origin of the acrid smell. The stench of urine was nearly overwhelming. Walking with crutches doesn't give the luxury of cupping your nostrils. Lloyd almost choked. Lila buried her face in one hand in a futile attempt to filter the air.

The stench of urine was nearly overwhelming.

The area was at least thirty feet square, with a twenty-foot ceiling. Heavy oval lights hung from long, thin poles. The floor, a faded black and tan check linoleum, was clean but showed severe wear.

A younger male voice could be heard in the distance. "Fuck you!"

A twangy older feminine voice closer to them spoke with ominous authority. "You better watch yur language!"

In clear defiance and even louder, the younger male shouted, "Fuck you!"

There was scurrying foot movement, a voluminous splash, and then a scream from the younger male. "You fuckin' bitch!"

People scattered as a bedpan, thrown from the source of the scream, crashed just beyond Lloyd and Lila.

Boinnng!

Both Lila and Lloyd jumped, but the orderly immediately sprang into action. He grabbed the still rolling bedpan and disappeared into the next room. There was some scuffling and muffled curses. Lila was horrified. Lloyd was at least relieved to see that the bedpan was clean.

With the voices quieted, it wasn't long before the orderly returned, this time a bit more disheveled. He directed Lloyd to a small room to the left, but they had to wait for stretchers and wheelchairs of varying makes and models to disperse before they could move.

There was a small desk, incongruous with the huge surroundings, with an even smaller lamp, which shed a bright light, wedged in the far corner. It faced a window that opened with a view into a larger room with many beds to the left. Straight ahead were two rooms, one on each side of a hallway leading to a bathroom. Various other windows, smaller rooms, and a hallway leading to another L-shaped room with beds were to the right.

One of the nurses greeted them, took Lloyd's little bag, and led him to a small tiled bathroom.

"This is our bathing room."

She was kind, but she was neither very old nor experienced enough to be the brains behind this outfit. Well spoken, she also wasn't the source of that southern twang Lloyd heard earlier.

"Everyone is bathed upon admission."

Lloyd was to learn this was not a bad idea considering the conditions and environments these patients called home.

The bathing room had a huge sink on one side, a clean tiled floor, and an enormous oval tub on a tiled platform in the center. Alongside the tub was an equally long and wide stainless steel changing table, also meticulously clean.

The young nurse instructed Lloyd to sit atop the changing table and remove all his clothes while the orderly filled the tub and added the right amount of soap crystals.

Lila seemed pleased to have an opportunity to exit. "Now, be good, Lloyd. Listen to the nurses and the doctors." Wrapping her arms around Lloyd with only a cursory hug, she left.

Lloyd was relieved to see her go. As with most hospital admissions, his independence began when his family relinquished control. This was also a chance to get to know the orderly.

The man assisted him into the tub and Lloyd decided to break the ice. "Excuse me, sir. What is your name?"

The orderly must have been shocked that one of his kids could speak so well, but he kept his answer short. "Danny."

Danny was in his early to mid-thirties. Short, with strong arms and just enough hair to cover his head, he was kind, but a man of few words. He assisted Lloyd when he was certain requests were too difficult for him to fulfill, or he would instruct Lloyd on exactly what to do, so there was nothing left to confusion.

This approach was impressive to Lloyd. He was accustomed to people who either stumbled and stammered, or were openly repulsed by him. Lloyd was only too familiar with reactions from "normal" people as if they were witnessing a Cyclops for the first time. Even people from the medical field sometimes reacted that way.

After stripping down, Lloyd had his temperature taken and was told that after his bath he would be weighed. Danny left briefly and returned with a stretcher. Behind him there was a bustling motion out in the foyer. The sound increased as the commotion outside reached the bathroom doorway. Despite his exposure, Lloyd nonchalantly turned toward the door and the source of the clamor, but couldn't believe what appeared framed by the opening. Completely unnerved by the sight, twisted, he froze in place.

The only way Lloyd could make out the sex of the individual standing before him was that the figure wore a white-skirted uniform. Formidable, she had little hair, and what there was of it, straight and limp, was shabbily pushed to one side. She wore a small, almost absent nurse's cap on the rear of her skull.

The woman's face was grotesque, the effect of pain and anger for far too many years. A pair of younger nurses flanked her, carrying out her smallest wishes without question.

Her head stood atop a huge torso that was almost perfectly round, her back arched to balance the bulging glob atop spindly legs. She had almost no neck and no breasts at all—nothing but her protruding belly. From Lloyd's vantage, she appeared nearly as round as she was tall. Her thin sticks of legs stopped at two wide, flat platform shoes that flopped and slapped against the floor with every step. Her gait could only be perceived by imagining a potbellied stove atop rickety branches, anchored by colossal webbed flippers moving from side to side.

Without a hint of kindness, she leaned backward, her piercing eyes fixed squarely on Lloyd. With almost total loss of control, he started to shake, as if cold. Once she was certain she held his attention, she moved quickly into the bathing room as though sliding on a high-speed rail. She leaned over him, quite literally blocking out all light.

As she stared at Lloyd, she quietly addressed her question to the orderly. "Was he wearing a diaper?"

Danny stood almost at attention. "It was one of those towel-wrapped diapers, super-saturated."

She never turned her face. Her glare remained on Lloyd. This time in a louder tone and more direct, she addressed her question to him. "How do you evacuate your bowels?" Her enunciation was a quick "e-vacute" and long "bo-wells."

Lloyd had only an idea what she meant. "I sit on the toilet and push."

Her face contorted. "Are you telling me you can control your stool?"

Lloyd didn't understand how she drew that conclusion. His answer was simple. "No."

"So... you poop your pants!" A small discharge of spittle sprayed his bare chest. She had meant to belittle him, and she succeeded.

Lloyd felt the sting. He believed that someday he might be able to control his bodily functions. This woman, like so many before her, was attempting to dispel those notions.

Over the years since the incident, he had sat on the toilet at regular intervals, pushing on his bladder to urinate, or trying to squeeze out a stool in a futile attempt to train himself. Always, the exercise ended in utter failure, despair and, more often than not, outright public embarrassment.

Lloyd's eyes began to bulge as he reverted to his acquiescent routine. He could tell it had no effect on the abhorrent form before him.

She bent down and with a raised finger pointed in his face, spoke with a craggy voice and strong coffee breath. "You listen to me, mister! If yur good..." She drew a winded breath. "...and do as yur told..." She took another breath. "...you and I will git along jist faan."

Her extended finger shook with every intonation. She spoke like she was emulating John Wayne. This was the twangy voice Lloyd had heard earlier, and the thought reverberated through his nerve cells.

She paused, again for effect. Lloyd was transfixed, as though in a trance. Then she continued. "If you don't do as yur told and yur not good..." she said, raising her fist for emphasis, her eyes squinting and glaring, her lips puffed with every word, "...I'll come down on you like a ton a bricks!" Her voice rose to a crescendo on the last word, drops of spittle spraying from her mouth.

The declaration ran a chill down the center of Lloyd's spine. The little hair he had on his head, thanks to Lila always insisting he have a buzz cut, stood on end. It was a warning he would not soon forget, a speech she had delivered many times.

This was Mrs. Gipe, who ruled Wards 14 and 16 with an iron fist. Nobody messed with Mrs. Gipe and lived to tell of it.

Mrs. Gipe ruled Wards 14 and 16 with an iron fist.

The origin of her accent was unknown. That was part of her mystique. It was rumored that she grew up on a farm down south. She neither revealed her educational history nor her influences. That would have made her vulnerable to the children in her care. No, Mrs. Gipe was a hard-line product of the institutional process. Her policy dictated that none of her staff discuss their personal life while on duty, and they strictly adhered.

She knew first-hand the environments from which these patients emerged. Starting from abject poverty, she had scratched and clawed her way up the work ranks, intelligent enough to say all the right things to her superiors to reach a position of authority. She was hard to the bone, but could turn on the charm when necessary. The children were always amazed when doctors made their rounds. "Yes, Doctor. No, Doctor. Have a wonderful day, Doctor." Mrs. Gipe's voice became so sweet and pleasant you would've thought some angelic host suddenly possessed her.

Where some might think she was a big fish in a little pond, being the head-nurse on the boy's ward was all she aspired to. The wisdom she bestowed upon those in her care was as Gospel as the Commandments brought by Moses from Mt. Sinai.

She neither cared if she were loved or hated, only that she be respected. She didn't need a manual to tell her what good manners were either. She demanded from the children and the people under her what she felt was right, and respect was highest on that list. She wasn't prejudiced or a student of political correctness. No, Mrs. Gipe's one true directive was the welfare and care of her charges—her kids. And, to that end, there was no equal.

She left the room with Lloyd shaking in her wake. Danny assisted him into the tub and also helped him scrub down. He had his orders as well. Not a crevice on a patient's body was left unattended. Mrs. Gipe would be sure of that. Lloyd was scoured with a heavy scrub-brush and lye soap from head to toe.

When finished (and only after Danny's close inspection), Lloyd was put on the stretcher again and rolled back out of the room and into the busy foyer to be weighed. In the midst of all the commotion in the lobby, he was left wearing nothing but a flimsy gown, open in the back, half naked and shivering.

Danny instructed him to move from the stretcher to a huge metal scale. It was apparent that Danny didn't worry how Lloyd would be able to do it. Here, the attitude was different. He was not treated like a baby or pampered with every request like other institutions to which Lloyd had become accustomed. And it wasn't just that he was 14 now and considered an adult. At this institution there would be no cajoling or coddling. Lloyd had entered a world unlike any other he had experienced or would ever experience again.

Kids from Allentown, Philadelphia, Pittsburgh, Harrisburg and remote parts of the northeastern coal-mining regions, all Pennsylvanians, were part of the mix. With ages ranging from 12 to 18 on the wards (younger kids were upstairs), here was a world of differing nationalities, cultures, a hodgepodge of disabilities and prejudices thrown together by the compounding confusion of bureaucratic shuffling and desperate families seeking help.

Desperation was the common denominator and what led all of them to the Crippled Children's Hospital in Elizabethtown, known as E-town. Cases of parents being ashamed of their children with a disability were commonplace. Although Lila had often told Lloyd that he would not amount to anything and that his whole existence was worthless, he realized early on at E-town that such thoughts and remarks were not unique.

Cases of parents being ashamed of their children with a disability were commonplace.

Unfortunately there still exists the idea that anyone with a disability is mentally deficient. All of the neuroses and psychoses that walk freely through life, able-bodied people are oblivious of their own physiological and psychological shortcomings, finding employment and enjoying the perks of society. Is it any wonder why the word "invalid" was used to describe someone with a disability? Is the life of an individual with a disability, with all of the foibles and frustrations he or she has to deal with on a daily basis, any less valid?

There were always repositories for societal rejects. Even during Christ's walk on earth, lepers were shunned and forced to find shelter in caves. Prior to the established State Institutions, there was a scenario common to people with disabilities known as hospital shuffling. In Lloyd's case he dealt with paralysis, without proper supervision, and had developed pressure areas on his body with skin breakdown.

After years of outright neglect and bone structure changes, coupled with bad posture, by the ripe old age of 12, he was a crumpled heap of curvatures and dislocated joints. The immediate concern for him was trying to heal the wounds, now bone-deep on his buttocks. After trying in vain through conventional means (keeping the area clean and dry), his family in a disjointed effort, consulted family doctor after family doctor. Rarely exposed to such cases in rural New Jersey where Lloyd lived, the general practitioners were hardly qualified to care for someone with such complications. In the early '60s, unless you lived in a large city where gunshot wounds were common and spinal cord injuries more commonplace, GPs were rarely exposed to such trauma, and consequent long-term chronic care.

In the case of Lloyd's skin lesions, the doctor suggested that his wound be cleaned and dressed daily and prescribed a little tincture of Benzoin to be applied to the dressing twice a day. The small bottle of Benzoin ran out quickly and the cost of dressings and Benzoin, available only in a pharmacy, were financially prohibitive to Lloyd's family. As his condition worsened, the general practitioner was called again. He prescribed another tincture and charged Lloyd's family again. This process continued for years, often resulting only in infection and intermittent fevers. His wounds deteriorated into severe ulcers, deep gaping holes in the skin, some right to the bone.

After months and months of this merry-go-round, the family doctor admitted there was nothing more he could do, and that the only recourse was that Lloyd be admitted to a local hospital as soon as possible. This began his hospital-shuffle treadmill.

Over time, plastic surgeons attempted to sew his lesions shut or take a piece of skin from another part of Lloyd's body and graft it to the affected area. Although the surgery, in some instances was successful, Lloyd always returned to the environment and conditions that created the ulcers in the first place—his home—so the pattern invariably repeated itself. Recidivism involving pressure ulcers is commonplace.

With repeated admissions to local hospitals and the strain on available insurance, the price tag was astronomical. To curtail costs, hospitals created what were known as Utilization Review committees, which exist in many hospitals to this day. Known as UR committees, usually consisting of a small collection of doctors, nurses, and/or administrators, they coordinated a patient's hospital care and assessed the degree of progress within prescribed objectives. For chronic conditions, such as the care required for a decubitus or pressure ulcer for instance, when healing is such a protracted process, it's difficult to assess progress in a few weeks.

When the Utilization Review committee decides a patient has made adequate progress, they work with Social Services (always with the authorization of the attending physician) to request the family pick up the patient, transport them to another facility, or take them home. There were no Utilization Review committees at E-town. It was understood that E-town was the final destination. And a patient had to prove their desperation before being admitted. That meant financial hardship.

For all of the paralyzed patients Lloyd would live with for the next five and a half years, this story would ring true. He was in good company. His trouble was that "good company" was not always so good!

TWO

NEVER UNDERESTIMATE AN OPPONENT

Like the eye of a storm, there is clarity of purpose,
a crystal focus amid enveloping confusion.

The wing Lloyd was taken to upon admission was composed of Wards 14 and 16, with a definite age difference between the two. Ward 14 was for boys aged 14 to 18. It consisted of twenty beds, ten beds to a side. Ward 16 was for younger boys aged 9 to 14, who were almost all direct transfers from the little boys' Ward 24, directly upstairs. Ward 16 had fourteen beds, seven on each side in an "L" shape.

Lloyd was led out of the tub room into the main working area of the floor, the foyer that had greeted him at the elevator. This was where he was weighed. In his skimpy gown, there was certainly not much left for modesty. Amid the maelstrom of speeding wheelchairs, stretchers, and beds of all sizes, Danny positioned his stretcher alongside a large, flat metal plate. He then instructed Lloyd to transfer onto the huge scale.

At over 500 pounds, the massive scale's base rode on a wheeled cart about three feet high. The platform was steel and painfully cold to a naked body, or at least a body that could feel it. Lloyd was paralyzed from the waist down and wouldn't notice. But he had to be extra careful to remain on the thin blanket Danny placed on the platform. He weighed in at a cool 65 pounds.

After Danny documented Lloyd's weight and had him climb back onto the stretcher, they had to wait for more kids on crutches, in fast-moving wheelchairs, and other patients in passing beds, before they could move beyond the foyer.

Strong, wiry men pushed stretchers at high speeds and around corners effortlessly. Their wheels were kept well greased and the beds moved freely, as though gliding on pockets of air. The men pushing them were exceptionally agile to avoid hitting people and objects.

After space cleared for them, Danny took Lloyd into a small room just outside the main bathroom. Two such rooms faced each other, with small wooden double doors that opened out. These were the isolation rooms. Lloyd was put in the room farthest from the nurse's desk. The room opposite his was empty.

Each room was approximately 6' by 8', with an outside window, running from mid-floor to ceiling, leading to a screened-in porch. The bare walls were painted a bright yellow. There was a bed in the far left corner, and a heavy, wooden, rolling platform holding a black and white TV to the right. The outer porch ran the length of the building. Ten feet wide, it had thick stone blocks topped by heavy-gauge screens that rose to the ceiling. Even if a patient considered escape, they would have to jump from the bedroom window, out onto the back porch, then hack through the heavy-gauge screen and drop fifteen feet to the forest floor. There were kids who tried it—even kids in wheelchairs!

Even if a patient considered escape they would have to . . . drop fifteen feet to the forest floor.

Separated from the main group of children, Lloyd was put in a state of reverse isolation because of his severe skin ulcers. He had the ability to attend school classes and therapy and to have people come into his room, but was unable to leave. That was part of his predicament, locked away without the benefit of other people for company. After meeting Mrs. Gipe, he was only too eager to make new friends. He had to find out what others thought of her, how much of a threat she was, and so on. He was about to become painfully aware that this small cell would be his home for the next year and a half!

Danny told him to move from the stretcher onto a steel-framed bed with a lumpy, plastic-coated, straw-filled mattress, apparently regular issue for institutional use.

Just sitting on the lumpy mattress with all the people scurrying around outside gave Lloyd a strange feeling of freedom. Each time he was admitted to a different hospital he felt a sense of empowerment that eluded him at home. The feeling that he could control at least part of his destiny became appealing.

Patients were not allowed curtains on the isolation room windows, but were given a rolling screen for minimal privacy. Nurses frowned on keeping the screen open because it blocked their view. With their extensive experience, they were always concerned that teenage boys, left to their own devices, would be up to no good. And their concerns were fully justified.

The isolation rooms were strategically placed. They created an enclosed hallway route to Wards 14 and 16's main bathroom. For anyone in isolation, watching the constant flow of patients was a great way to meet people. Although a few kids rolled by and looked, obviously checking out Lloyd, Tom Dreher was the first to actually slow to a stop in his wheelchair.

Tom was an interesting character. Although appearing the same size as Lloyd, Tom was much thinner, but his arms were muscular from pushing his wheelchair too many years. With thick black hair pushed to one side, and glasses two sizes too big, Tom gave the appearance of the bookworm type.

"My name's Tom. What's yours?"

"Lloyd."

"Whatta ya in for?" It was a common question for all new kids. And, Tom, who had already been in the hospital for some time, had heard it all.

"Bad sores on my bottom and a lot of other stuff."

"Are you paralyzed?" Tom could tell just by the way Lloyd was sitting in his bed.

"Yeah. I'm a paraplegic. How 'bout you?"

"I'm Spina Bifida."

"Spina-what?"

"I was born with part of my spine exposed. Parts of my body are paralyzed, too." Tom was honest and very open. That was his way. "Were you born paralyzed or hurt somehow?"

This was a new twist to the same old question. Lloyd was tired of it. People outside the medical world aren't as sensitive. Lloyd would have to get used to this approach while at E-town.

"I was shot in the back."

This took even Tom by surprise.

"You were shot?" He laughed. "Jesus, how?"

Lloyd wasn't sure how deep he should go with the answer. "With a gun."

"A gun? What kinda gun?"

"A shotgun."

"Jesus!" Tom shook his head in disbelief, his eyes bulging, almost as though he wanted to ask more questions, but knew how uncomfortable he was making Lloyd. He continued a bit more calmly. "Did they tell you how long you were in for?"

Lloyd wasn't sure whether Tom was referring to his being in isolation or the hospital. "They said I'd only be here for a few weeks."

Tom laughed and tried to hide a smirk. "They always tell the new kids that. I guess they just don't wanta scare 'em."

Now Lloyd was scared. "Whatta ya mean?"

Tom had seen other kids break down with the reality. But, here, it was always better to pull the band-aid off fast. "I haven't seen a kid stay here any less than six months, and I've been here more than eight months myself."

Speechless, Lloyd just stared at him. Tom had no reason to lie. Hell, they were all in the same boat anyway. As with most kids though, Lloyd was convinced he'd be the exception rather than the rule. All new admissions thought that.

"Well, hang in there," Tom said to soften the blow. "You never know."

With that he laughed again, turned his wheelchair around and was gone. Lloyd was left with an empty feeling of dread. He didn't have long to lick his internal wounds before he noticed a small group of kids forming at his door. It was kids from the back Ward 16.

Lloyd was convinced he'd be the exception rather than the rule. All new admissions thought that.

Kids from Ward 14, being older, were a little more diplomatic. They often got the younger Ward 16 kids to find out information on the new kids. Again, the same range of questions came: "What happened to you?" "Whatta ya in for?" "How long did they say you'd be in for?"

Starting to enjoy the attention, Lloyd answered all of their questions. Then he noticed some inappropriate giggling going on in the crowd. One of the kids wheeled forward. "Hey, you want to join our gang?"

Lloyd was game. "Sure!"

With that, two kids in wheelchairs scurried away and shortly thereafter, a different kid wheeled himself around the corner. This was Marvin Sparks. Marvin was a veteran of the hospital. He had been there far too many years and had known how to treat "new kids."

Marvin was paralyzed in both legs and one arm. With complete arrogance and without introduction, he wheeled straight as an arrow, moving his good hand from wheel to wheel, keeping the chair rolling perfectly forward. Straight up, he didn't even bother to brake—Marvin rammed right into the side of Lloyd's bed.

Lloyd was startled, but impressed. He had never seen precision with a wheelchair like this before.

Marvin was one of the tougher of Ward 16's group, and clearly their leader, establishing his superiority with newer admissions. This not only brought new kids into line, it reinforced his dominance over fellow patients. Where Lloyd's only interest was to fit in and find some modicum of acceptance, Marvin held no such allusion. He had been raised in a dog-eat-dog world and dispatched his dominance as coolly as an alpha wolf in a pack.

He was one of those kids who would always be a threat, even outnumbered or under a pile. Lloyd's measure of Marvin only represented a sad disability fallen on hard times, much like himself. Lloyd felt that no one disabled and within his own age bracket was as tough as him, so no one could be that great a threat. Lloyd tried to open him up with a simple question. "Whatta you in for?"

Marvin gave no answer and no introduction. He wouldn't even give his name or make eye contact. He simply locked both wheels, pinning his chair tightly against Lloyd's bed.

Lloyd tried again. "What's your name?"

"I'm not tellin'!" Marvin shot back loudly.

He didn't have to. His henchmen had already filled in the details and sat quietly, right behind him. Apparently Lloyd wasn't submissive enough for Marvin and, with the small group of minions watching his every move, he obviously had a reputation to uphold. Marvin finally spoke. "I'll bet you're not as tough as you think you are."

Now, Lloyd was thinking, *This kid's startin' to bug me.* "Oh, really!"

"You're gonna have to be initiated in order to join the gang."

Lloyd thought about it. Sure, he'd like to join whatever gang there was just to have friends, but what that meant was always spelled out in the fine print. Lloyd had been in gangs before. He was smart enough to know that in order to join some gangs there were many things he would just not do.

Marvin continued. "I bet I can kick yur ass!"

Lloyd knew that talking trash could always escalate into something physical so you always had to be ready. He had experienced much of that on the streets of Allentown, Pennsylvania, and Lloyd's brother had always been his toughest opponent. But, checking out Marvin's physical ability, Lloyd did not want to fight this guy. With Marvin's having only one usable arm, he didn't think there was any way this could be a fair fight.

"I don't want to fight you," was all Lloyd could think of to say.

With that there was a chorus of jeers from the group that had formed behind Marvin.

"Whatta ya, chicken?"

"He's just scared."

"Whatta baby!"

Without thinking, Lloyd's only retort was, "Hey, it's not gonna be a fair fight. He's only got one arm!"

Well, if ever Lloyd said the wrong thing, that was it! The crowd jeered even louder.

Marvin sprang into action yelling, "Come on, mother-fucker! You think yur so tough!"

He began swinging at Lloyd, and although having only one usable arm, he was Lloyd's size, and amazingly accurate. He nailed Lloyd on the left shoulder and upper arm a few times, but Lloyd was able to duck most of the shots. If he tolerated the barrage for a little while, maybe this guy would tire himself out and call it a draw.

Although having only one usable arm, Marvin's aim was amazingly accurate.

That was not happening. After a few minutes of Marvin's swings and Lloyd's ducking, they weren't really making any progress. When it became apparent that Marvin wasn't tiring, Lloyd reached over to grab Marvin's arm.

That was his first mistake.

Marvin's still flailing arm was remarkably strong and he was able to keep Lloyd from holding on to it. He used a technique foreign to Lloyd at the time to free himself, something akin to karate. Whenever Lloyd reached for his hand, without much effort, Marvin twisted it, pulled back, and was able to throw Lloyd off. As he did, Marvin swung again and caught Lloyd with a shot to the chest.

Lloyd's frustration built and he decided it was time to end it. But he would have to get closer to pin Marvin down.

That was his second mistake.

In his attempts to grab and hold on to Marvin, Lloyd's attention was diverted. He completely underestimated Marvin's resourcefulness. While Lloyd groped to incapacitate Marvin's one good arm, Marvin cunningly reached around the back of his wheelchair and grabbed the thick black cord of the television set that extended from the wall. With one swift looping swing, he smacked Lloyd square on the top of his head with the plug.

It stung so bad, Lloyd recoiled. "Hey!" he yelled, as though pleading would somehow diminish the pain and slow Marvin's onslaught. No such luck.

Without missing a beat, Marvin swung the cord again like a whip. He was remarkably deft. Welts were already forming on Lloyd's shoulders and back. The pain of the blistering pummel took its toll. Marvin was beating Lloyd to a pulp!

In a last gasp effort, while absorbing another blow to his midsection, Lloyd grabbed the cord, pulled it taut, and adroitly wrapped it around Marvin's good arm and one corner of the wheelchair.

Marvin struggled to free himself but couldn't. When Marvin realized he was unable to move, he began spitting at Lloyd, who recoiled and openhanded a hard slap across Marvin's face.

It must have hurt because Marvin yelled, "Hey, you fuck! Cut that out!"

Marvin was almost entirely immobilized. Mad and spitting, he tried to head-butt Lloyd. Unlocking the wheels of Marvin's chair, Lloyd turned it around then cautiously untied Marvin's good arm and pushed him and his wheelchair toward the door.

"Get the fuck outta here, now!"

All this happened while remaining quiet enough not to arouse the nurses' attention, but emphatic enough to make it clear to Marvin that Lloyd meant business. This brought out a roar of laughter and applause from the crowd.

Just as forceful and not as quietly, Marvin, whose wheelchair slammed into the edge of the doorway, spit back at Lloyd again. "Fuck you, cocksucker!" With his hand free, and noticing the momentary loss of popularity, Marvin wheeled himself out of the room.

Relieved, Lloyd was left alone again, rubbing the growths atop his head and shoulders, trying to make sense out of what just happened. He learned a very important lesson about fighting though. *Never underestimate your opponent!*

Lloyd learned an important lesson about fighting... Never underestimate your opponent!

Ward 16 and Marvin Sparks initiated Lloyd, but he was to learn that this rite of passage was mild in comparison to most of Ward 16's initiations. Usually if a kid wasn't submissive enough, as soon as the nurses went to lunch or supper break, all the guys would pounce on him. However many kids it took would hold the new boy down, spread-eagle, and strip him naked. The leader would beat his body (in parts where he could feel) with a heavy wooden ruler until welts formed. If the kid screamed and tried to fight too much, they would hold him even tighter. Then some boy would climb up on the bed and bite down hard on the new kid's testicles so he was certain to have something to scream about. Often this was repeated several times until the new boy learned to conform to peer group rules such as no tattle-taling, no talking back to leaders, and no crying or other infractions of their jungle law.

It wasn't long before Lloyd began to realize many aspects of his admission that were blessings. One small but significant one was his isolation.

As formidable as the confrontation with Marvin and Ward 16 proved to be, his challenges weren't over. Lloyd had to deal with kids closer to his own age and older, from the front Ward 14.

THREE

A FRIEND AND A VERY SPECIAL VISITOR

*There is always someone smarter, stronger, faster, and
far more compassionate. In spite of overwhelming odds,
regardless of being right or wrong, it is the individual
least afraid to make mistakes who leads most effectively.*

E-town had its own in-house school from kindergarten
through grade twelve. It also had its own in-house
hairdresser and dentist, as well as a full staff of training
surgeons who performed surgery on the premises.

Shortly after admission, Lloyd took a few aptitude tests and,
after careful examination, entered the ninth grade. School was
in the morning. Physical Therapy filled his afternoons and
evenings were spent getting to know people passing his door or
just sitting alone watching his big black and white television.
Initially, he was transferred from his bed to a stretcher and then
taken to a classroom. Within a few days however, they
transported him in his bed with its rickety four-inch wheels.

This was an exercise reserved for the few gifted men who
could navigate the long hallways and shoddy elevators. Drawn
from the custodial staff and dressed in press-starched dark-
green shirt and pants, these men held the unenviable task of
transporting patients to their destinations on time. Strong, thin,
wiry and moving at a frenetic pace, they were always writing
down assignments to keep track. It was remarkable how they
maneuvered such clumsy vehicles without destroying corners,
walls, or hitting anyone.

One such man was George, a custodian. When he wasn't washing or waxing floors, because of his strength and intelligence, he also transported beds and wheelchairs. A heavy smoker, he was tall and thin and moved with the grace of a gazelle. George also possessed the unique ability to acquiesce to the demands of administrators, while at the same time, being kind enough to patients to give them adequate time to prepare to be transported. This was a delicate balance.

Administrators didn't care whether patients were ready for transport. If a patient had to be in a schoolroom or the therapy department at a specific time, they wanted them there. Older teenage patients took a bit longer to prepare themselves before being transported, and so demanded more time. George always respected that, often taking the associated heat.

Stretchers, narrower than beds and with larger wheels, were easier to push and easier to steer, but all beds, stretchers, and wheelchairs were required to be driven sometimes hundreds of yards throughout the hospital.

Patients were rarely schooled or had therapy in their respective wards. Most had to be moved from all over the institution—four girls' wards and four boys' wards—on two separate floors, to and from classes and therapy as well as the surgical and recovery areas. All had to be coordinated at varying times each weekday. Staff and visitors constantly dodged an array of beds and wheelchairs, and within this frenzy, many patients were forgotten or late. Though George had help but not much of it, if a patient was late or forgotten, it was George that took the blame.

Lloyd liked George and was always ready to go. George was also a recovering alcoholic. Lloyd's parents were heavy drinkers and his mother loved her cigarettes. They rarely visited and that hurt deeply, so the thick smell of cigarettes on George's clothes, and his very noticeable morning shakiness, elicited strong memories of Lloyd's mother and he felt a deep kinship with George. They struck up a fast friendship.

It was those memories of his parents in the month of April 1965 that triggered Lloyd's first deep depression. Mrs. Gipe was aware of Lloyd's sadness and called Mr. Jared Stewart, the newly hired Director of Activities to speak to him. Mr. Stewart was a psychologist, read Lloyd's history, and agreed to help pull him out of his funk.

Lloyd had just come back from one of his morning classes when Mr. Stewart arrived at his room. He was carrying Lloyd's chart when he knocked, his nose buried in paperwork. Mr. Stewart was a short, stocky man in his mid-30s, which to Lloyd, made him appear just another venerable old man.

Lloyd greeted him cheerfully. "Come in."

Noticing the open folder and casual dress of the gentlemen, Lloyd could only assume it was another hapless hospital administrator fulfilling a duty to satisfy empty blanks on endless reams of paperwork.

The gentleman took a chair from the corner and moved it to the center of the room. As he sat, he looked up from the chart. "Lloyd Neg...o...oski?"

"Neg...o...es...cu."

The man smiled. "Mind if I just call you Lloyd?"

"Lloyd's okay." Lloyd liked that this new man had tried to pronounce his name.

"Well, my name is Jared Stewart. I'm the new Activities Director. I've been reading your chart and it looks like you've really had a lot of hard luck. It says that you haven't gotten along with your stepmother. Is that true?"

"I guess." Lloyd didn't know what this guy's angle was. Experience told him to be wary of opening up too quickly with administrators.

"It says in your chart that you were... 'unmanageable'." He paused and emphasized the last word.

Lloyd didn't say anything. He just bowed his head.

Mr. Stewart continued. "Do me a favor, Lloyd. Read this statement." He handed Lloyd a small piece of paper with words printed large on it.

Lloyd took the paper, studied it for a moment, and then read out loud, "Ladies and gentlemen, please welcome Mr. Danny Thomas." He read it straight through, without skipping a beat.

Mr. Stewart smiled and leaned back in his seat, dropping his hands and the patient chart on his lap. It was as though he had searched the entire kingdom and finally found the owner of the glass slipper.

"Perfect!"

Lloyd was speechless, but happy that he obviously pleased the man.

Mr. Stewart stood and methodically placed Lloyd's chart on the nightstand. He turned, grabbed his chair, and pulled it closer to Lloyd's bed, announcing, "I have a proposal to make!"

Lloyd didn't know what a *proposal* was.

"How 'bout this? The Shriner's Circus is coming to Elizabethtown Crippled Children's Hospital in three weeks. Their main star this year is Mr. Danny Thomas. Do you know who Danny Thomas is?" The man grinned from ear to ear.

"Do you know who Danny Thomas is?"

Lloyd's interest piqued. "Yes. I always watched *Make Room For Daddy*. Danny Thomas looks a lot like my dad."

"Well, it just so happens that Mr. Danny Thomas is coming here to the hospital to do a show."

Lloyd didn't know how to react. He wasn't even sure he would be allowed to see Mr. Thomas or the show.

Mr. Stewart continued. "We're going to get all the kids from all the wards in the entire hospital and fill the big auditorium and have a show!"

Lloyd still didn't understand his part.

Mr. Stewart, still grinning from ear to ear, spoke in a quiet tone. "Lloyd, I want you to be our Master of Ceremonies."

Lloyd was nonplussed. He didn't know whether he should be happy or sad. "What's a Master of, of... what?"

"A Master of Ceremonies. That's an individual that stands on the stage and introduces the guests of a show. You'll be the Master!"

Still perplexed, Lloyd was beginning to infuse Mr. Stewart's excitement. "A Master of Ceremonies." Lloyd repeated it several times just to remember the words. "Master of Ceremonies. Master of Ceremonies." Still, he had no idea what it meant.

Mr. Stewart wasn't deterred by Lloyd's flat acceptance. "Don't worry about that. You'll do just fine."

"But, sir, I can't stand. The nurses say I have to lie down when I'm on the stretcher."

"Oh, that won't be a problem. You can lie down. Just try to memorize those words I gave you and repeat them over and over again. Ladies and gentlemen, please welcome Mr. Danny Thomas."

Lloyd pulled the paper closer to his eyes and read aloud. "Ladies and gentlemen, please welcome Mr. Danny Thomas. I don't know, sir. I might mess it up."

Mr. Stewart stood up. "Just keep repeating those words and you'll do fine!"

He quickly gathered his papers, returned the chair to the far corner of the room, came back to Lloyd's bed, shook his hand softly, and said, "Keep your chin up. We're going to have some fun. I'll be in touch." Then he briskly walked out of the room.

Lloyd was left wondering what that whirlwind was all about. He knew who Danny Thomas was and that the actor was coming to the hospital, but he couldn't be sure when or if he could memorize those words in time. Mr. Stewart seemed like a nice guy. But what was that word? Master of sell-a-mony, or sell-mony, seller-ony?

Turned out the event wasn't for a few weeks. For the first few days, Lloyd studied his line every free moment. As the weeks passed he was left wondering if Mr. Thomas was even coming. When the event neared, the thought of seeing Mr. Thomas was almost entirely forgotten from Lloyd's mind.

When the day finally arrived, Mrs. Gipe was meticulous in bathing Lloyd herself that morning. She combed his hair, what little there was of it, and found him a nice light-colored shirt. The stretcher he was placed upon was adorned with crisply ironed white sheets of varying lengths. After she was sure she had done all she could to make Lloyd look special, she called George for transport to the auditorium.

When George arrived, Mrs. Gipe gave him his instructions.

On the way, George said, "Boy, it seems you got the top spot today!"

Lloyd still wasn't sure what he had to do. "Yeah, they want me to keep saying something over and over again. I still don't know what it's all about."

"Well, they picked you. Nobody else. And Mrs. Gipe's got you all gussied up, that's for sure!"

Lloyd wasn't sure how to feel. In a flat tone he said, "Yeah."

When they arrived at the auditorium, beds from all over the hospital were being placed strategically around the room. Larger beds were further to the rear so as not to block the view, while smaller beds, stretchers, and wheelchairs were up front. A narrow path remained open around the perimeter for late arrivals and, of course, Mr. Thomas himself.

George greeted one of the nurses directing traffic. "This is Lloyd. He's supposed to go on stage. Where do I go for that?"

She pointed to the far end and said, "Take him over there. There's a ramp leading to the stage in the back. Take him up and place him in the center of the stage looking out."

Ever faithful, George did as he was told and pushed Lloyd's stretcher to the far corner, up the ramp in the back, right to the very center of the large stage. Lloyd looked like a skinny fledgling on a bed of white down feathers.

The auditorium was at least 2500 square feet. In the time it took George to get Lloyd across the room, navigate the stretcher to the rear and up the ramp to the center of the stage, the room was almost entirely full. Mr. Cooper, the shopkeeper and part-time soundman, came up on stage and handed Lloyd a microphone.

"Now test this. Say, 'test, test' and talk normally."

Lloyd repeated the words, "Test, test." It broadcast loud and clear throughout the room.

Mr. Cooper said, "Good. Speak clearly and right into the microphone so people can hear you." With that said, he turned and walked off the stage.

It was both frightening and exhilarating to look out upon this vast sea of people and bed-frames. When the room filled it was standing room only. All beds, stretchers, and wheelchairs of various makes from all corners of the hospital, all personnel, administration, and nursing staff alike, everyone and anyone showed up or were transported to see Danny Thomas.

On stage, all alone, holding the microphone was Lloyd on his stretcher, only equipped with a single line to address the crowd.

It was standing room only. Everyone showed up to see Danny Thomas.

He joked with some of the patients. The nurses up front asked who he was and he told them. Lloyd was having a good time talking to people when, from the rear of the room, there was a large clatter of hands and cheers. From his vantage point, Lloyd couldn't tell what was happening until those flanking him allowed Mr. Thomas to proceed through the maze of humanity and metal. The guest shook every extended and non-extended hand and arm, hugging and kissing people as he weaved his way to the stage.

This was the moment Lloyd began a barrage of his well-memorized line.

"Ladies and gentlemen, please welcome Mr. Danny Thomas."

"Ladies and gentlemen, please welcome Mr. Danny Thomas."

"Ladies and gentlemen, please welcome Mr. Danny Thomas."

It was novel at first, but Mr. Thomas walked slowly, returning everyone's greetings on his way while folks clapped and cheered. Lloyd's repetition of the phrase dwindled into a droll monotony.

By the time Mr. Thomas reach the stage, everyone was exhausted from clapping, but that did not deter Lloyd's pleadings.

"Ladies and gentlemen, please welcome Mr. Danny Thomas."

"Ladies and gentlemen, please welcome Mr. Danny Thomas."

"Ladies and gentlemen, please welcome Mr. Danny Thomas."

As the entertainer climbed the stairs to the stage, he was smiling. He leapt across the stage and, after hugging and kissing Lloyd on the cheek, accepted the microphone. The room erupted in exuberant applause.

Everyone but Lloyd was relieved Mr. Thomas made it to the front. Lloyd, on the other hand, couldn't get over how much this man resembled his father. He even smelled like Lloyd's father. As Mr. Thomas was releasing Lloyd from their hug, Lloyd began sobbing uncontrollably.

Mr. Thomas could see the embarrassment on Lloyd's face and made a joke. "If you think I gotta big nose...!" Then, in his gruffest Jimmy Durante voice he added, "...take a look at dis shnoz!" And he kissed Lloyd on the head again. Lloyd laughed with everyone else.

Mr. Thomas was the consummate entertainer. He spoke freely, told jokes, and even sang a few songs. In his five-and-a-half year stint at E-town Hospital, Lloyd would not meet a more gracious, more warmly received individual than Mr. Danny Thomas.

Buoyed by the event, the other kids still teased Lloyd about repeating his phrase too many times. George thought he did a great job and Lloyd's relationship with the custodian grew exponentially.

With his family experiences and George's willingness to share, they both talked openly about a wide range of subjects, especially what liquors were best and what cigarettes they liked. Lloyd's knowledge consisted of whatever he'd gleaned from his parents' use.

One morning as George maneuvered Lloyd's stretcher out of the isolation room and beyond earshot of the nurses, Lloyd noticed a pack of cigarettes in George's breast pocket. "I see you're a Marlboro man."

While straining to maintain control of the stretcher, George asked Lloyd, "Do you smoke?"

"I could use a smoke," Lloyd lied. He had smoked a few times, but only to impress girls at his local pool.

Without a moment's hesitation, George reached into his pocket, pulled out the pack of Marlboros and handed it to Lloyd who quickly shoved it under his sheet. Cigarettes were a strict no-no. If Mrs. Gipe ever got wind of it, Lloyd would be in deep trouble.

When returned to his room, Lloyd hurriedly hid the pack in the back of his bedside cabinet drawer and paid no further mind to

Cigarettes were a strict no-no. If Mrs. Gipe ever got wind of it, Lloyd would be in deep trouble.

them. It was enough status with the other kids that Lloyd even possessed such an unlawful substance.

It wasn't long before Lloyd started meeting not only all of the boys from Ward 16, but also the boys of the front ward, Ward 14. Word spread of his encounter with Marvin Hawks, and it wasn't long before challenges from other kids filtered back to him.

A few days after the Danny Thomas event, Mrs. Gipe told him that he would no longer be fed in his room. "Big boys don't eat in their room. From now on, you'll have lunch with the other boys in the playroom."

Mrs. Gipe often ordered able-bodied patients to the playroom for lunch in hopes that by getting them out of their beds (even those placed on stretchers) and out of the ward, they would learn to become more independent and less inhibited. It was conversely true that when patients wanted to eat in the playroom, however, they were rarely allowed. In fact, patients only ate in the playroom for a short time. Whatever was in Mrs. Gipe's mind at the time was what would play out.

There was a definite method to her madness. As long as she could continue to change whatever she thought the patient wanted, she could maintain discipline by keeping them off guard. She took pride in laughing at patients the more confused they became. Within her sphere, Mrs. Gipe was the only true authority and she certainly had a grasp on how to control teenagers—always keep 'em guessing!

The playroom was a 10' by 20' room with a TV and stereo with two of the largest speakers Lloyd had ever seen. As with all things donated to the hospital, the administration could not control the quality, shape, or size of an item. The speakers were huge and mounted high on the wall on either side of the turntable. The stereo control, however, was quite primitive. It consisted of only two knobs—one for power and volume and the other for speaker balance. Each knob was part of the turntable mounted on the wall, low enough to be accessed by someone in a wheelchair. There were two variables for speed, 45 and 78 RPMS.

The irony of such a construction was not lost on the staff and, more importantly, Mrs. Gipe. Here were teenage boys, in varying stages of age and levels of rebellion, given full access to a stereo system with speakers so large and powerful that, on full volume, they could literally peel the paint off the walls. The crowning absurdity was that the patients were instructed to keep it turned down or face severe penalties.

"You'll keep it down, or spend the rest of the day in bed!" came Mrs. Gipe's warning. A warning rarely, if ever, observed.

Danny, the orderly, came to get Lloyd with a stretcher and, as he wheeled him toward the playroom, smiled and said, "Watch out for Gary Tates. He's wiry. And he's the one that throws the bedpans."

Lloyd remembered the day he arrived and the bedpan that rolled past him and Lila. "Thanks."

> *"Watch out for Gary Tates. He's the one that throws the bedpans."*

As they entered the playroom, Danny whispered, "You'd better put this T-shirt on or Mrs. Gipe will get mad."

Lloyd looked at the faces of the other kids in the room. Danny's words were well within their earshot. They were all staring and wondering what Lloyd's next move would be.

"I don't want to wear a T-shirt."

Just as the words left his mouth, he heard an angry voice from the other side of the room. "Hey, buddy, put your T-shirt on and follow the rules!" The voice belonged to Gary Tates, and like the boy himself, was harsh and cold.

Gary was the toughest kid on Ward 14 at the time. He was either admired or feared and was considered a legend to the little kids upstairs in Wards 24 and 26. Gary was paralyzed from the waist down. As a result of severe infections, some of which lasted for years, he was forced to have both legs amputated above the knees.

He was bitter, having been a patient there most of his life, always fighting other kids and the administration. Gary had heard about Lloyd's run-in with Marvin Sparks. The version of the story he'd heard was that Marvin kicked Lloyd's ass, so Gary was primed. He wasn't about to have Lloyd or anyone else challenge his authority.

Lloyd knew that if he were going to get anywhere in the boy's ward hierarchy he'd have to tangle with Gary at some point. *The sooner the better*, he thought.

Lloyd looked him over. Gary seemed as tough as they came. And he was. Gary was the product of too many institutions. His family had long since given up on him. He never received visitors, so there wasn't anyone he respected or cared about. There was little the higher-ups could do to threaten him or bring him in line for all his nastiness. Mrs. Gipe's remedy was always a bucket of cold water.

With long strong arms, Gary had at least 20 pounds on Lloyd. In spite of his loss of legs, he was someone who knew how to drag himself around with remarkable ability. The fact that he had no legs made him that much more agile. Like an ape, he could jump from the top to the bottom of his bed with lightning speed.

Where most patients would lift themselves with the flat part of their palm, Gary used his closed fists. And he always kept both hands fisted with his arms straight at his sides so he could appear taller. The outsides of his knuckles were worn and as rough as shoe leather. His hands were a visible warning that, if you ever get punched, it was gonna hurt!

Despite the threat, Lloyd knew he would have to make a statement of defiance to show that he was not one to back down. All he could think of was the courage it took to endure years of daily abuse from his older brother. Cold and cruel, whenever he'd disapproved of what Lloyd was doing he uttered a phrase that meant there would be painful consequences. Someday in the not too distant future, late at night or early morning, wide-awake or in a deep sleep, there would be a reckoning.

As Danny wheeled Lloyd out, he turned to Gary, raised the index finger of his right hand, and with eyes squinting said, "I owe you one, buddy. I owe you one!"

Lloyd didn't see very much of Gary after that, but he heard through the grapevine that Gary wanted to fight him. Lloyd's reply to anyone passing the rumor was, "Anytime, anyplace. Right now is just fine!"

FOUR

YACK COMES TO E-TOWN

*Levels of intolerance increase with
equal measure our levels of ignorance.*

Within a few days of Lloyd hiding the pack of cigarettes in his nightstand for safekeeping, Leonard Yackilowski was admitted to E-town. With his amiable gift of gab, kids quickly named him Yack-Yack, which was eventually shortened to just Yack. Born with Spina Bifida, he developed pressure ulcers on areas of his feet he couldn't feel. After repeated surgeries, he was finally admitted to the Crippled Children's Hospital where he could get the care he required without further financial hardship to his family. At that time, he had casts on both feet up to his knees.

Yack was raised in the northern coal-cracking regions of Pennsylvania. His father was a coal-miner and Yack carried that with pride like a shield of armor. Where therapists and teachers ruled from beyond the wards, with the exception of Mrs. Gipe and the nursing staff, there was always one kid in each ward who dictated the ultimate flow of the group. Yack was bound and determined to become that kid. What he lacked in formal education, he more than made up for in street intelligence and bravado. He wasn't the toughest, or even the smartest, but he possessed the innate ability to manipulate groups. They put Yack in the isolation room opposite Lloyd.

Some of the stricter nurses on duty would not allow Lloyd's and Yack's doors to be open, Mrs. Gipe, of course, spearheading that group. At night though, the nurses were a little more lax.

41

The boys could pull their beds to the edge of their doorways as long as no other patient accessed either of their rooms. When able, boys in isolation always did this to talk in the early evening.

This time it was Lloyd's turn to question the newcomer. "My name's Lloyd Negoescu. What's yours?"

"Wow, that's a mouthful! Mine's Len... Yackilowski. Len."

"Heh, Len. You have a long last name too! Whatta ya in for?"

"Surgery for sores on my feet."

Lloyd noticed that Len could move his legs, so he assumed the new boy wasn't paralyzed.

Len turned it on Lloyd. "Whattar you in here for?"

"A whole lotta stuff. How'd you get sores on your feet?"

"I can't feel them, so I couldn't tell there was too much pressure before they broke down." But Len was curious. "What whole lotta stuff?"

"I got sores on my bottom, my hip's dislocated, and they say my spine's crooked."

"Wow. How'd you get so fucked up?"

"I was shot in the back when I was nine."

"Really? Who shot ya?"

"My brother."

Len looked surprised, but didn't show it much. He seemed much more worldly than most of the kids there.

Lloyd went further. "You can move your legs, so you're not paralyzed. How come you can't feel your feet?"

"I don't know. It's the way I was born... Spina Bifida. I don't really understand it myself. Just that you're born with part of your spine open, that's all. So, what's with you? Are you paralyzed?"

"Yeah. From the waist down."

"So, you can't feel from the waist down?"

"Nope."

"Not even your dick?"

"Nope."

"Can you get a hard-on?"

"No."

"Well, that sucks." And, with that, he chuckled.

Lloyd's head bowed.

"Hey, don't feel bad, Ace. Gettin' a hard-on's not all it's cracked up to be."

Lloyd was curious now. "Whattiya mean?"

"When I was at this other hospital and they had to shave me down there for the operation on my feet, they sent in this big-titted blonde. She had tits that wouldn't quit... gorgeous!"

Lloyd sat up straight now.

Yack continued. "So, this broad comes in with a tray and says, 'I have to shave you, now'." Yack threw his tone high in immitation. "Her voice so sweet it could melt butter! So, I'm layin' there thinkin', all right, she's gonna shave around my feet since that's where they're operatin'. Next thing I know, she's throwin' off my blanket and pullin' down my underwear!" Yack started to laugh.

> *"Getting' a hard-on's not all it's cracked up to be."*

Lloyd giggled too, not really knowing where Yack was going with this.

"So, then she reaches down and grabs my Johnson." Yack reached for his crotch. Lloyd had never heard the term before, but he got the gist.

"And she starts washin' me." Yack started to laugh louder now, which made Lloyd look around to make sure there were no nurses present.

"Well, she's washin' and washin' me, and I'm starin' at those boobs and how nice it would be, and..." He trailed off, like in a stupor.

Lloyd leaned forward, close to falling head over heels over the end of his bed, hanging on Yack's every word.

"Next thing I know, she's got the razor in her hand and she's shavin' me." It was as though he were talking about a dream.

His eyes began to roll up in his head and his legs started to twitch. The whole atmosphere mesmerized Lloyd.

Yack regained his lucidity. "I didn't know it at first, but I was startin' to get a hard-on. I mean a hard-on so hard I could cut coal! I knew I was excited, but I was hopin' I wouldn't get a boner on top of it! Well, sure enough..." He started to laugh out loud again, this time more forcefully.

"Next thing I know, she's got the razor in her hand, and she's shavin' me."

"So, now I'm tryin' to think of somethin' other than her boobs, somethin' stupid, like baseball, but it's no use. I'm rock hard now, and she's holdin' on to the tip of my dick..." Here he extended his arm with his hand pointed down, in a pinching position. "...while I'm tryin' to get my mind offa her!" More laughter.

"Then, it happened." He continued to laugh.

Lloyd was confused. "What?"

"I started to jizz." He laughed "Not only that, but my dick was shaking and I started laughin'..." Yack was laughing much harder now. "Here she's holdin' on to my dick out to here..." He extended his arm. "...Movin' her head, dodgin' the spit, and my shit is startin' to slide down her hand..." He laughed louder and gestured the flow moving down his hand. "...and... and her face is turning all shades of gray, and she's lookin' at me like I'm some kinda bug!"

Yack's words just trailed off in a fit of laughter.

Lloyd laughed too, but had no clue what it must have been like.

It took some time for Yack to recover from laughing so hard. He was literally crying and coughing at the same time. "Oh, man! I dunno..." He wiped his eyes and pulled his hospital gown backwards, open in the front, out from underneath him. He coughed again and straightened up.

Lloyd just watched as Yack worked to compose himself.

"Oh man, just to see her face! I mean she looked at me like it was my fault. Shit." He pulled himself up, coughed a little more, then wiped his hand through his hair and used the end of his gown to wipe his brow.

Lloyd didn't say anything, just sat staring.

When it was quiet again, Yack continued. "Do you jerk off?"

This took Lloyd off guard. "No, not much." Lloyd never did.

"Well, I've heard that if you jerk off enough, you can get the blood to flow and get a hard-on."

Now, Lloyd was surprised. "Really?"

"Hey, it's worth a try. What de hell."

Lloyd was happy. "I'll give it a try."

It was shortly thereafter that it was time to turn in and the doors to the isolation rooms had to be shut for the night. Once the lights were out, Lloyd did "try"... for almost an hour, but to no avail.

Mrs. Gipe was wary of Yack's newfound popularity. He was a tough kid, but always polite to his elders, almost an Eddy Haskell like on *Leave It to Beaver*. Mrs. Gipe kept a close eye on both Yack and Lloyd. When Lloyd was in class, she went in to his room and rifled through his nightstand. She would do that, just to stay on top of things because you could never be too careful dealing with teenagers.

Sure enough, she found the pack of cigarettes Lloyd received from George. She studied them for a bit, then methodically placed them back, exactly where she found them, remembering to arrange all the other items in their original position as well.

When George brought Lloyd back to his room before lunch, she watched intently. As soon as George left, she was the first to enter. "Hello there!" she greeted in her gruff voice.

"Hi." Eyes wide, Lloyd was always on alert where Mrs. Gipe was concerned.

She stepped from the doorway, flopping her feet toward him. She focused her gaze on him as she neared his nightstand.

"Do you have anything to tell me, young man?" Her tone was sharp and accusatory.

Lloyd knew he was in trouble, but had completely forgotten about the cigarettes, so he scrambled for something to say.

He thought, *I must've swore or something! It's always swearing that gets me in trouble! Damn! I better play it safe and not say anything!*

"No." A soft tone was all he could muster.

Without another word, she went straight to ransacking his nightstand. Digging deep, she knocked out half of the contents, pencils, erasers, paper clips and such, some of which landed on the floor. Lloyd could only watch in horror as she yanked out the pack of cigarettes.

Holding them in her open palm, she thrust her hand in front of his nose. "Whatter these?"

Her hand was shaking. She was clearly upset. This

Lloyd knew he was in trouble, but had completely forgotten about the cigarettes.

could be the "ton of bricks" she'd warned him about in her opening speech. Lloyd knew he couldn't deny the cigarettes. He knew very well what they were.

In a timid, almost silent voice he answered, "Cigarettes?"

Mrs. Gipe's gaze riveted on his, and her hand continued to shake as she crushed the pack before his eyes. He could smell the tobacco and winced with the crackle of the paper wrapping.

In a softer, but much more forceful tone she asked, "Do you have any idea how serious this is, young man?" She didn't wait for an answer and leaned closer, almost nose-to-nose. "We don't allow cigarettes here!"

Lloyd didn't say anything. His frightful gaze, one he had honed skillfully under his stepmother, was a cross between abject fear, despairing sorrow, and Bambi vulnerability.

It must have worked because Mrs. Gipe's overbearing browbeat softened.

She stepped back and stared at the cigarettes, now a crumpled heap in her hand. There was a long quiet pause. Without a word, she leaned back on her heels and turned and looked over at Yack in his room. Yack could see what was happening and had already moved to the edge of his bed to get a clearer view.

Lloyd shifted too, and could see Yack looking over, but he didn't have a clue what Mrs. Gipe was thinking.

She looked back at Lloyd and said ominously, "Where did you get these?"

> *"Do you have any idea how serious this is, young man?"*

Lloyd was schooled, again taught by an overbearing brother, never to reveal a source, even by threat of death! Without a word and not losing the intensity of his repentant stare, he just shook his head in feigned wonder.

Mrs. Gipe turned to look at Yack again, this time raising the fist holding the cigarettes in Yack's direction. She yelled, "I know these are yours!"

Yack only raised his arms in question. Frustrated, he turned and crawled to the other side of his bed.

Lloyd pleaded, "Mrs. Gipe, they're mine!"

She was adamant. "Don't you cover up for him!" And with that, she turned and stomped out of the room.

Lloyd watched as she threw the crumpled pack in the garbage can by the nurse's desk. He glanced over at Yack, but could only make out a lump of sheets; Yack's head was buried under his pillow.

Later, Lloyd apologized for the mix-up. "I'm sorry you got blamed for my shit."

Yack just smiled. "Thanks for tryin' to take the heat offa me, Ace. Get used to it. I get blamed for everything!"

And he was right. From an administrative point of view, Yack was judged more by his socio-economic status than his own character, which to them did not shine too brightly. Lloyd felt sorry for him and admired him.

Yack was upset, but pleased he had been given credit for sneaking in the cigarettes. It added to his street cred with the rest of the ward. It didn't take long for him and Lloyd to form a deep abiding friendship.

FIVE

THE GREAT POW-WOW AND YACK EDUCATION

Mob rule demands its own agenda.
Those who oppose it and are not consumed by it
are strengthened as a result.

The main group of kids on the wards ostracized the boys in isolation. A number of hierarchies existed, including kids who looked up to other kids for protection and support. There were prejudices based upon age, ethnicity, intelligence, and the severity of physical condition. Those involving age, ethnicity, and intelligence are commonplace and self-explanatory. Explaining the prejudice that exists among varying degrees of disability is harder. Too often people in the "real" world look at someone with the slightest disability as also having mental incapacity. Kids at the Crippled Children's Hospital, even though disabled themselves, adopted these precepts as readily as a manner of speech.

Lloyd had already challenged the hierarchies of both wards and now Yack was testing control as well. So, as the two were confined to their isolation rooms, word got out they were troublemakers, a captive audience whom boys from both wards could tease on their way to the bathroom. Many had no intention of fighting, but leaders of their respective wards egged them on.

If Yack's and Lloyd's isolation doors were open, kids spit at them, threw water at them, or made faces or snide remarks as they walked by.

"Look at the isolation boys in their cage."

"Hey, it's monkeys at the zoo!"

Yack, always the innovator, developed a method to equalize the cultural divide. He created the "Slam Book," a loose-leaf binder with personal-taste questions at the top of each page. At the beginning of the book an individual is instructed to sign their full name and pick a number. That number then designates them. Their answers to each question on succeeding pages were identified by their number. Each kid was free to add their own question at the top of a new page with their answer and corresponding number beneath it.

Most questions were generic in nature, for example: "What's your favorite color?" or "What's your favorite rock band?" But some were more introspective. "Who's your favorite nurse?" and "What was your worst day and why?"

The book was a way to solidify the wards. In some instances it worked. Kids from both wards began to share their ideas with each other in a more open fashion. It was an effective tool for Yack to learn about everyone because the kids' answers were revealing. When Yack finally retrieved the book, he studied it and no one saw it again. But it didn't surprise Lloyd that with the advent of the Slam Book, Yack's popularity increased profoundly.

Yack created the "Slam Book," a loose-leaf binder with personal-taste questions.

Furloughs were granted to a few kids who were ambulatory, to go home to their families on Friday night, under the stipulation that they return to the hospital by five o'clock Sunday evening. But when Sunday came, with pangs of leaving their families again, the kids who returned raised the already high frustration level of those left behind.

One sultry Sunday night in the summer of 1965, the returning kids gathered with others in the playroom for a "pow-wow," an impromptu meeting.

The stereo was cranked, playing 45RPM records donated by local radio stations after songs dropped in popularity. Wards received boxes and boxes of these six-inch discs they had to sift through. A patient would take one of hundreds of records, play it to hear if the song sounded good, and depending on who was listening, then save it or discard it. Only a few were kept by consensus of the group, and the process was laborious so many ended up resenting the merchant's gesture.

The pow-wow was heating up in the playroom as the furloughed and remaining kids commiserated about their respective hardships. The boys had formed a tight-knit community since visiting hours were only every other weekend for two hours on Sundays, and many patients had little or no family visiting them. They became their own collective cell. If one guy called a nurse a dirty name or struck one of the staff, they were all affected. As a result, the staff cracked down on unruly behavior by curtailing the activities of them all rather than just the perpetrators. That was Mrs. Gipe's way of having the boys police themselves—an effective, but cruel practice.

That Sunday night, with intensity unlike anything previously experienced, one of the kids grabbed a stack of 45s and started sailing them across the playroom like Frisbees. Upon impact, the thick plastic records chipped gashes two-inches in diameter as they bit deep into the "green monster," what the patients called the hunter-green walls. This began a free-throwing festival that ended in the total destruction of the playroom walls. Piles of broken 45s commingled with hunks of plaster. The nurses shrieked in horror when they saw what happened. All activities were summarily suspended and everyone was ordered to their beds.

One of the kids grabbed a stack of 45s and started sailing them across the playroom like Frisbees.

Ward 14 was shut down. All activities, beyond schooling and therapy, were curtailed for an indefinite time. Even furloughs were discontinued. All transistor radios were confiscated and the television was unplugged. All the kids on Wards 14 and 16, with the exception of those who were able to go to the bathroom, had to remain in their beds. Silence in both wards was strictly enforced.

This period of bleak despair lasted almost two months. A whispered pact between the wards dictated that no patient, beyond necessary compliance—eating, bathing, or following medical protocol—would cooperate with the staff. That meant that any patient caught by other patients fraternizing with the staff would experience severe punishment and ostracization.

This was no easy call. Leaders from both wards instructed their groups to adhere to their edicts or risk severe backlash. However, a few of the leaders on each ward held relationships with certain members of the staff that were more than intimate and they were not about to sacrifice that. Thus, their edicts were directed at their underlings, not themselves. "Do as I say, not as I do."

Few kids passing the isolation rooms stopped to give Lloyd and Yack the news. The positive effects of the Slam Book had almost completely worn off. From his vantage, Yack could see the damage occurring in the playroom and cheered them on, but most of the boys routed to the bathroom stepped up their level of harassment against Yack and Lloyd.

Yack's idea to combat the abuse was the "cattail."

Yack's idea to combat the abuse was the "cattail"—a long thin towel wrapped tight diagonally, two feet long with a tail, split at one end. Lloyd had to be taught how to make one and Yack was a very good teacher. After he learned, Lloyd even formed a small handle he could wrap around his hand to prevent the possibility of dropping it.

Yack said, "Don't worry, Ace. We'll get these bastards!"

Lloyd practiced for hours, snapping everything in sight. He found he could crack so delicately, he could kill flies with one swat.

The boys made them just long enough that with their beds pulled tightly against the edge of the door, they could easily reach each other's cattail end. From every angle, they could ensure that passersby would not be allowed free access to the bathroom without getting smacked coming or going.

Lloyd practiced for hours, snapping everything in sight.

It worked. Even the more aggressive patients began to back away from the isolation boys. For a time, hostilities against Lloyd and Yack slowed to a crawl.

With harassment reduced, days passed with relative ease. It was mid-summer and, since there was no air-conditioning, temperatures in the little rooms became stifling.

Yack and Lloyd had to keep their windows open, even during bad storms. The thick screens on the porch were porous. Bugs could get in and out with little or no restriction. At night mosquitos had free reign to dole out their stinging attacks. While it was extremely hot and they had to strip down, Lloyd and Yack found it necessary to soak their sheets with cold water and wrap the sheets around themselves just to sleep without being stung.

Before lights out at 9:00 PM, their nightly ritual remained the same. Yack would signal Lloyd with a high shrieked whistle. Having the right nurse on duty, Yack and Lloyd pressed their beds against their doorframes and held court over their bedposts, talking for hours. The conversations always began with Yack.

"What's happenin', Ace?"

"Hey."

"Do you know what pussy smells like?"

"Sure."

With a smirk, Yack thought Lloyd was lying. "When did you ever smell a pussy?"

"I told you, I had this girl named Lisa."

"Come on. She never let you touch anything, did she?"

"We used to make out for hours."

"Well, what'd it smell like?"

"I don't know. It was different..."

"You're wet behind the ears, Ace. You don't know shit!"

"Oh, really? Well, what did you ever do?"

"I fucked my sister, that's what!"

Lloyd laughed. "You what?"

"Well, she wasn't exactly my sister. She was kinda my half sister. My mother and father divorced and I ended up livin' with my father and his new wife and her daughter. I never got along with my old man's new wife, She was an ol' *battle-axe*." The bad feelings he had for the woman, regardless of how much she may have helped him, reminded Lloyd of Lila, his stepmother.

Yack continued. "She hated me. She made me wear these big-ass diapers made outta towels."

Lloyd knew exactly what Yack was describing. "Me, too! And I had to wear 'em when I was in school too. I hated that! They stuck out like a giant pile in my pants. My stepmother never liked me either."

Yack's bravado took over. "I didn't pay no mind. She'd bitch at me for pissin' and shittin' all over the place. I didn't give a shit!"

"Yeah, I know about that, too. After school I'd have to dry myself off before I went inside. My stepmother would always grab my crotch to see if I was wet."

"Yeah, this ol' battle axe, too! Anyway, she had this daughter. She was 17, with long red hair and big tits. God, what tits! I used to try to catch her on hot days, when she'd come out of the bathroom. Damn, her nipples would stand on end!" He was starting to laugh. "She'd catch me starin' and give me a dirty look."

He laughed again. Yack had a great laugh. His laughter was so infectious, people had to laugh with him,

"This girl was so fuckin' horny, she'd be fuckin' all the time. She'd fuck her boyfriend in the backyard. It's not like she did it where nobody could see or hear. We'd be asleep, and all of a sudden, the whole house would be awake with this junk car we had parked in the backyard, rockin' all over the place! And she'd be screamin' when she came! This girl would be in there almost every night with her boyfriend, fuckin' like rabbits!" He laughed uncontrollably at this point. "That junk car was old and rusty and creakin' real loud, and drove everybody inside nuts!" He laughed so hard he had to stop for a while.

"Didn't your dad go out and yell at 'em?"

"In the beginning, he tried. But she was so horny, she'd be fuckin' the next night anyway. She ended up pregnant and had a kid. Then my father really got pissed, 'cause her boyfriend took off. My ol' man thought, 'Shit on this. I don't need another mouth to feed!' He was no dummy! But the ol' lady put 'er foot down and her daughter stayed with the baby. So the ol' man cut 'er off. He wouldn't let any guys come round."

Yack, although he adored women, had classic outdated ideas about them. Lloyd was impressionable and in a feeble attempt to be more popular, he tried desperately to adopt Yack's ideas for himself.

As they were talking, Duffy pulled up in his wheelchair.

"Uh-oh, here we go," Lloyd said.

Duffy was a thalidomide victim. He had tiny little arms and short legs. He was able to propel himself in a wheelchair with his legs dangling. Whenever he was teased, which Yack loved to do, Duffy would flap his arms in a futile attempt to smack someone. This was how Yack came to give him the nickname "Flipper."

"Hey, Flipper! Wass happenin'?"

"Don't you call me that!" Duffy had a pressured speech effect. If he got angry, he literally spit when he spoke. "That's not my name, and you, you're, you're, you're a bad person!"

Yack could not leave well enough alone. "Hey now, I didn't say anything. Don't start on me, Flip!"

"Stop it!"

And, with that, Duffy spit on Yack. This only fed fuel to the fire.

"You spit on me, you fuckin' pig!" Yack grabbed his cattail and snapped it at Duffy, catching him just above the ear.

When attacked, Duffy (aka "Flipper") would flap his arms in a futile attempt to smack someone.

"Ow! You, you, you, rot...en, rot...en..." The spit was really projecting now, as Duffy fumed with anger.

Lloyd knew this could only get worse. "Yack, leave him alone!"

"He spit at me, the freak!"

Duffy was still spitting, and now barking and jerking spasmodically in his wheelchair. "Ro, ro, ro, rotten! Ro, ro, ro, rotten! Ro, ro, ro, rotten!"

Yack snapped his cattail at Duffy, landing some stinging blows. Duffy was beginning to lose it. His head and face were red and he gasped for air.

Lloyd knew he had to do something, but couldn't reach the boy. Duffy was too close to Yack and still spitting. Lloyd had an eight-foot pole in his room, used to open windows closer to the ceiling in the big wards. He also used it to move his bed around the room and pass the time learning how to twirl. So he grabbed this pole and extended it out to Duffy's wheelchair, latched onto the boy's front tire and pushed him out of Yack's reach and further into the boy's bathroom.

Duffy was surprised. "Hey, wha-wha-what's goin' on?"

Yack gave Lloyd a bad look, but Duffy's crisis was averted. "Hey, what da fuck? Get him back here, da fuck!"

Lloyd calmed Yack by distracting him. "Finish the story about your sister, or your half-sister."

"Geena."

"Yeah, Geena, with the big tits!"

Yack was still flustered, but they both laughed. "Yeah. Well," He caught his breath. "The ol' lady told me that since I wasn't in school, I had to watch the baby. So, it was all right. I got along with the kid real well. He's a good kid."

Lloyd wanted to hear more.

"Okay, okay. Cool your tool!"

With his right casted leg bent under his left casted leg in front of him, Yack leaned back and ruffled his gown to let in air.

"So the baby's in Geena's room and I'm watchin' 'im. I'm sittin' there on the floor playin' with the kid's toys with 'im. The whole house is empty, 'cause the ol' lady and ol' man are at work and my other brothers are in school. I couldn't go anywhere. So, me and the kid are playin', and in comes Geena. She quit school when she was 16. She had a part-time job, but mostly hung around the house, too. She walks over and smiles at me. Now, remember, her boyfriend took off and she's been cut off dating by the ol' man, so she's hornier than ever! She looks down at me on the floor and bends over so her robe opens up a little. I'm checkin' it out, but don't say anything. Just smilin'."

With that, he beamed a big grin on his face.

"Then, she whispers to me, 'Hey, you wanna fuck me, little man?' I say, 'Little man? Yeah!' So, she goes over and lays on the bed, opens her robe and spreads her legs. I jump up and I can't believe what I'm lookin' at. I throw my diaper off, and run up on the bed so fast it scares 'er. My dick is so hard I can hardly stand it. Anyway, I get up to her. She puts me in and starts buckin' up and down. We're goin' at it what could be 'bout three minutes. All of a sudden, the door opens downstairs... it's the ol' lady!"

My eyes got wide.

"Geena pushes me off her so hard I fall on the floor." Yack laughs. "I'm rushin' round lookin' for my diaper, and the footsteps of the ol' lady are comin' up the stairs! Geena jumps off the bed and is already in the bathroom, so she's safe. I grab my diaper, tryin' to get it on, but the pin pulled out."

In those days, everyone used giant safety pins to close diapers.

"Anyway, now I'm wonderin' how I'm gonna explain this! I pulled my pants up, and they held the diaper, so I was all right. The ol' lady never mentioned it."

"What about you and Geena again?"

"Again? Shit, she wouldn't even look at me after that! Like I had the plague or somethin'. I prob'ly pissed on 'er. Damn, she had nice tits though!"

SIX

THE GREAT ESCAPE AND YACK'S BET

There is that element in nature that compels us all to move mentally, physically, or spiritually. Whether it is forward or backward, even though we may appear or sense that we are a body at rest, we are always in motion.

The weather grew colder as 1965 drew to a close. The sun had just set, and Yack and Lloyd, with beds pressed against the edge of their doors, were having an ordinary evening talking about their favorite subject—sex. Ready to strike anyone who passed with their cattails, whenever one of the nurses jumped up from the desk and rushed over, they pushed their beds back into their rooms and abruptly slammed their doors shut.

"What's the problem?" Yack protested.

"Never mind," was the only response.

Yack and Lloyd just stared at each other in disbelief. Lloyd maneuvered his bed back into its required position. As he did, he noticed one of the kids from the back ward sneaking out and creeping closer to his rear window. Lloyd carefully looked to see what the nurses were doing and, when the coast was clear, he slowly opened one of the windows.

The kid was crouched low, hidden from view and breathing heavily. His whispered voice was shaky. "You... you won't believe what happened."

"What?"

"T-t-two kids from 14 took off. The nurses... sh-sh-shut down the ward tighter'n shit."

59

"What do you mean they took off?" Lloyd asked

"They escaped! I gotta go."

With that, Lloyd heard the kid's footsteps diminish. As Lloyd closed the window, he was left with a strange feeling. *Only prisoners use the word "escape." What is it about this place I should worry about? And where do kids go when they escape?*

These questions and more plagued all the boys throughout the evening. Kids approaching the bathroom came to Yack and Lloyd and reported on the ongoing turmoil. Their remarks always ended with, "...and don't say shit!"

The nurses were noticeably upset, moving erratically, with administration officials questioning them and others. Obvious questions were raised regarding supervision and oversight.

"You won't believe what happened. Two kids from 14 took off!"

Kids all over the hospital were upset. Everyone could see the stepped-up police presence. And it didn't take long for the story of the two who left to filter throughout the building. All were put on heightened alert.

The few boys of Ward 14 who had an inkling of the plan never let on. There had been extensive discussions of how to get out if you wanted to. Few of those left behind thought someone would actually try it.

While most of the kids were frightened, leaders and kids who had been there the longest were proud someone had the guts to go through with the scheme. Out in the real world, things were changing socially, but inside the institutional cocoon, there was an indoctrination that authority should be given the highest degree of respect. Newbies, and even those who remained loyal to their families who had no other medical recourse, were scared that conditions in the hospital could become much worse.

They also feared the inevitable backlash. *Would activities be suspended? Would visiting hours stop? Would those in power shut down the building? And if they did, where would they send us?*

Hours passed and still no word. State Troopers and local police mulled around, discussing ways to lock down the grounds to prevent future unauthorized departures.

After what seemed like an eternity, two kids—one walking rather jerkily on crutches, the other in a wheelchair—were escorted by police to Ward 14 past Lloyd's and Yack's rooms. The two looked disheveled and beat. Their clothes were ripped and dirty. They moved slowly and kept their heads bowed. The police didn't even let them go to the bathroom alone. Their every movement was scrutinized. In any other environment, you would have thought them criminals. The only things missing were shackles.

Lloyd looked over at Yack who was sitting on the edge of his bed. Where the horrific scene shook Lloyd, Yack merely grew angry and flashed the police the "bird" when they looked in at him. The cops shook their heads in disgust, but remained vigilant.

Yack merely grew angry and flashed the police the "bird" when they looked in at him.

The escapees had this planned for months. They conspired without assistance to leave right before dusk. They had been gone well over an hour before their departure was noticed, at least by the staff. Like most of the kids, the two were frustrated with the level of care they were getting. After months of wrangling with the idea, they came to the conclusion that the only way to survive was to get out of the hospital and try to make it on their own, wherever that led them.

These were not physically fit kids. The one on crutches had a cast on his leg from the knee down. The other had a longer cast on his leg all the way up to his hip. The boy with the longer cast couldn't even walk. His only mobility was in a wheelchair.

When they had left the building, they remained on the main road until they spotted the police. They then entered the thick surrounding forest.

The one walking helped the one in the wheelchair. They climbed over and around shrubs and brambles and over tree stumps. The kid walking broke his leg cast. The other, in the wheelchair, busted an axle and had to crawl. The State Police found them huddled, shivering, buried beneath a bed of dead leaves and moss behind a rotted downed tree. They were deep in the woods, a good quarter-mile from the hospital.

Both had families that tried to help, but were ill equipped to deal with the issue. The boys wanted out, but under the financial burden their physical disabilities demanded, their families could not afford to keep them. They, like other boys at the time, felt abandoned. They did not consider the Children's Hospital their home, nor the staff their family. They had no allegiance to the people in whose care they had been placed. They never gave a definitive reason for their quest, only that they had to leave the grounds when they were convinced they couldn't get permission through regular channels. They were summarily discharged to their families and restricted from ever applying for readmission.

Everyone's nerves were shaken after that. The tension in the air was palpable. Security was beefed-up in the building and the surrounding grounds. This meant hiring a guard to patrol, locking down outside doors at sundown, and increasing supervision. Whatever had angered the two to such a degree to attempt such a quixotic quest permeated the atmosphere of Wards 14 and 16. While patients may have had valid reasons of their own, the administration had no clue.

Although the kids acknowledged that there were severe conditions they had to endure to get the help they needed, most agreed they would not want to jeopardize their admission status. There were a few kids who still relished the idea of escape—Yack, in particular. Like most older teenagers, he didn't appreciate strict rules.

The isolation rooms were approximately seven feet on a side with eight-foot ceilings, overbearingly hot in the summer, uncomfortably cold in the winter, separated by a thin four-foot strip of linoleum that led to the older boys' washroom.

With their beds pressed against the open doorway, and hunched over their bedposts, once Yack started to speak, it was as though he were a preacher conducting a sermon. The bottom of his half-painted, steel-framed bed served as his makeshift pulpit.

At times, he could draw a group of curious seekers of "Yack truth." One late afternoon when the weather was warm, a mob gathered in front of Yack's door. What surprised Lloyd was the conspicuous absence of nurses. One group had taken an early dinner; the remainder was taking a smoking break in the closed hamper room.

Lloyd moved his bed to the edge of the door to find out what the clamor was about. The common topic was usually sex and Yack, being the "man of the world," controlled the lectern. Today's topic, although still about sex, was a bit different. Yack had made the boast to the crowd that if he had to, he could achieve a full erection from a limp "noodle," unaided by handwork or props of any kind, within fifteen seconds.

> *Yack boasted he could achieve a full erection from a limp "noodle" ... within fifteen seconds.*

"You're full of shit!" was one response.

"You couldn't do it on a bet," was another.

"I got money says you can't do it!"

Money always piqued Yack's interest. He spoke up without hesitation. "I'll take any and all bets!"

With that, there was such a demand that Yack, who had no funds at all, looked to Lloyd for help. He knew Lloyd had money.

Lloyd looked at him with an expression that read, "Can you really do this?" Yack's return look was sharp and discernable—complete affirmation.

"Bring all your bets to me," Lloyd replied to the group. "I'll cover any bet. I think he can do it!"

Kids were crawling all over each other to reach Lloyd's door.

Lloyd scrambled to get his tablet and pencil to write down the names and amounts. There were so many kids demanding bets, Lloyd started to panic. "Okay, okay! Only bets 25 cents and lower!"

Kids with more money were upset, but Lloyd knew he could only carry so much.

> *"Bring all your bets to me," Lloyd replied.*

Those kids enlisted others who had no money, just to be able to win more. Some smart kids asked for better odds, but Lloyd made it clear that winners would be paid even money. Some even wanted to bet their clothing, but Lloyd only took cash.

Yack smiled as he watched Lloyd feverishly write the names down with their individual amounts.

The next issue was that they needed a timer. A watch was produced, a nice big one with a large second hand. They also needed someone impartial, and most importantly, whose honesty was beyond reproach, who would watch the time.

It wasn't too hard to find someone. They had Lurch.

Lurch was a little kid named Kevin who had a degenerative muscle disease that made him look like Lurch from the Addams Family. Kevin was only 13 and all of the muscles in his body had atrophied. Even the ones in his face, so his cheeks sank below his chin. Lurch was dying. He was thin, could not move his legs and, over time, could only sit up hunched over in his wheelchair, which he propelled with his hands very slowly.

Lurch always insisted on doing as much as he could without help. If you ever got behind Lurch, out of respect you had to wait for him. He was proud, intelligent, and loved by all.

Most importantly, Lurch could never tell a lie. He was honest to a fault. So they positioned Lurch right in front of Yack's doorway, holding the watch.

When the rest of both boys' wards heard about the bet, all who were capable crowded the hallway and both porches outside each window, thankful the nurses were on break.

There was a crush of bodies and wheelchairs pressed against Yack's and Lloyd's doorways when Yack announced, "All right, I need a little time to get my head together."

This brought an immediate clamor of boos and hisses from the already restless mob.

"Aw, come on!"

"He's gettin' scared!"

"Cold dick!"

Lloyd shut everyone up with, "He's just gettin' into position!"

Everyone's eyes were riveted on Yack who had strategically placed his bed in the very center of his room to give the crowd the best vantage point. He removed his gown and his 4-stringer—a square piece of fabric with four strips of cloth sewn to each corner, used as underwear, that could be easily placed and replaced over casts and braces.

Carefully shifting all the pillows to one side, Yack laid flat with his legs dangling off the side of the bed, facing Lloyd's room. His penis was limp, and with the barrage of clatter from the mob, his body turned a deep shade of crimson. He kept moving from side to side, making sure the lumps in the bed were forced out and he could position his body as loose as possible. He ran his hands hard through his hair, and pumped his arms across his chest as though he were preparing for a boxing bout.

There was another loud clash from the crowd.

"I want my money back!"

"What, no popcorn?"

Yack was concentrating with everything at his psychological disposal, and despite the difficulty, patience from that crowd was impossible. Finally after a brief pause, with his arms extended and his hands clenched, he gave the thumbs-up signal to Lurch to begin timing.

People were screaming with a fevered pitch when Lurch, with limited breath, yelled, "Fifteen seconds and counting!"

Lloyd, whose voice could be heard over the din, yelled, "Think about sex, Yack! Think about sex!"

What was going on in the head of that 15-year-old boy was pure sexual delight. Whatever it was had to transcend the immediate attention demanded by the crowd. Whether it was the shaving nurse or his stepsister Geena, how he could have maintained any duration of clear thought amid all of the confusion puzzled everyone.

> *"Fifteen seconds and counting!"*

But his penis was responding with each descending count.

"14..."

"13..."

Lloyd yelled, "Quiet, quiet, we have to hear the time."

"SHUUUT-UP!"

The crowd quieted a little, but it was still hard to hear Lurch's count over the noise.

"12..."

"11..."

The flaccid appendage began to twitch and undulate from side to side in a slow uneven coil. Yack extended his arms with clenched hands at his side as though some force off the edge of the bed restrained them. His body shook and his hips moved rhythmically left to right. His breathing intensified with each count. His legs were taut, and even the tips of his toes in each cast twitched.

"Nine seconds!"

"8..."

His hands broke the perceived restraint and Yack started rubbing his face fiercely. His hips jerked, his legs vibrated and with each quake, his penis started its exhaustive climb. Lloyd was amazed at the progress Yack had already made. Lloyd also began to think that in eventual failure, it was still a valiant effort on Yack's part. With seven seconds already gone, an erection was beginning to form.

Of all the stories told by Yack—and there were many which may or may not have been true—whatever that boy had running through his mind in that short duration of time was not folly. He was totally entranced in whatever personal experiences he'd had with women, and there couldn't have been too many because he wasn't that old!

Conjuring up all the senses of smell, sight, taste, sound, and touch he had enjoyed became real. The simple recollection of Yack's most erotic sexual fantasies materialized. Most thought he was willing his penis to rise on purely monetary grounds, yet Yack's thoughts were geared toward the most salacious images he could conjure.

His mouth stretched back almost to the lobes of his ears, breathing as hard as he could, panting and heaving, heaving and panting. His elbows pressed hard against the stiff mattress which had already begun forming a perfect outline of his body under the strain.

His chest rose and fell with every inhale like a giant piston. His nostrils flared wide, and he snorted like a racehorse on the third turn. The muscles in his thighs and buttocks were pulled tight, and the veins on his arms popped like nightcrawlers.

His nostrils flared wide and he snorted like a racehorse on the third turn.

Yack pumped his hips and murmured in a slow cadence, simulating plunging his member deep into something beautiful, and with each pump, his legs quivered as though struck with electrodes.

Well over 20 pairs of eyes were glued to the one instrument that had caused more discussion of manhood through the ages than man himself. All thoughts geared to the mechanics of the object, the penis, and its ability to perform within a 15-second time span, were clear. Could Yack live up to his own great expectations? Was he man enough to admit that there were some things even Leonard Yackilowski could not do?

As though they had all been hypnotized, transfixed, caught in a vortex of increasing excitement, it was as though nothing could detract them from their collective focus. But, as focused as they were, an explosion akin to an atomic bomb detonated and shook them all.

BOOM!

Everything stopped short. Within the electricity and frenzy of witnessing this surreal event, something combustible choked off all sound and movement. Even Yack jerked in reaction.

If this were the interruptus, absent the coitus, that side-tracked the progress Yack was making, all bets would have to be off. Within a split-second, almost all turned to witness a heavy steel bedpan roll across the floor and smack against the wall opposite the nursing station.

CRASH!

Gary Tates, frustrated with the lack of attention paid to him, had tried to throw a monkey wrench into this peculiar machinery. All acknowledged the sound and then, almost in unison, heads turned back to the task at hand. Yack was un-fazed. If anything, it provided just enough interruption to allow him to refocus.

The kids worried that if the nurses noticed, they would stop the entire process. In fact, the nurses were alerted by the clatter of the bedpan, so they rushed to confront Tates, completely distracted from the proceedings.

This gave the group adequate time to finish the contest.

Lurch's diminutive voice continued the count.

"Seven seconds!"

"6..."

"5..."

"4..."

With three seconds to go and all paying audience members positive they would make a bundle, this small, uninhibited hard-ass (pardon the pun) from the coal-crackin' regions of Pennsylvania, was rising the proudest, award-winning erection anyone would ever witness... those, of course, inclined to do so. But Yack's penis was not totally erect yet, and the agreement was that he had to have it up completely stiff and ready to perform to win the bet.

As the seconds counted down, the crescendo of shouts and sneers rose, and Yack's groaning and grunting were becoming less and less audible over the tumult. Those present were engulfed in a cloud of stagnant fog, a mixture of Yack's sweat, his urine and pre-cum, and the multiple farts he expelled under the strain. Compound that with the cornucopia of incontinent onlookers and their body odors and you had a veritable bouillabaisse of putrid septic, none of which made the slightest difference to the captivated crowd.

"3..."

"2..."

With one second to go, Yack let out a whaling, guttural scream, absolutely primal in origin, that shocked all the skeptical onlookers, and gave his penis the final surge of blood required to stiffen to rigidity.

The boy did it!

Amid the screaming, shouting, and hand clapping, Yack achieved an erection quicker than most—a 15-second time-lapse from a completely limp position, unaided by props of any kind. Lloyd was amazed, but also pleased he hadn't lost any money.

Apparently, Yack had surprised himself. He commented later, "I really wasn't sure I could do it. I knew I was quick, but I never thought I was that quick!"

Drenched in perspiration, his body shaken, red and weak, his bed soaked in sweat and urine, he sat catching his breath as Lloyd gathered all the money. It was an experience those present would never forget.

All winnings went to Yack. Lloyd could have taken a percentage, but felt that Yack deserved the money.

SEVEN

FIRST CHRISTMAS AND A SPECIAL FRIEND

All too often we are summoned
by that which we most desire.

At the close of the summer of '65, the doctors operated on Lloyd's decubitus—bed sores—and they were healing nicely. Most often occurring as a result of prolonged pressure in specific areas of the body, including the spine, coccyx or tailbone, hips, heels, and elbows, people confined to bed with the inability to turn themselves are most prone to developing decubitus. Depending upon the severity of the wound, they may range from Stage 1, which is a pinkish color on the skin warning of excess pressure, to Stage 4, deep cavities severe enough to affect internal organs. Lloyd's decubiti were located on the cheeks of his bottom and ranged between Stages 3 and 4. They were so severe that upon admission his body had been riddled with infection.

Resident doctors, on their rotations through their specific surgical specialties, performed the operations. Specialists who supervised them often had to intercede when performance on the operating table became dicey. Kids were never told who would be operating on them. Often, the doctors who diagnosed a condition were not around long enough to perform the surgery they had ordered.

Lloyd's operation was a skin graft, known as a "flap." Because the cavities on his buttocks were so deep, surgeons scraped the dead and rotted tissue, then shifted and attached fatty tissue from the remaining portions of his already skinny behind to the affected areas.

After the surgery it was imperative to keep pressure off those areas to allow them to heal. Lloyd's bed was equipped with a steel frame and blocks. He would be on his stomach all day, seven days a week until his wounds healed.

A steel frame bed was six feet long and two feet wide and wrapped with thick pieces of canvas, tied underneath with strong intertwined roping. Placed on top of two 4-inch square, three-foot blocks of wood at opposite ends of the mattress, the canvas pulled taut, was open at the bottom and center.

Lying on one's stomach, a male patient could hang their feet off the end of one section of canvas, and their penis and testicles in the center section. The upper section of canvas supported the torso. If they had no bowel or urinary control, a bedpan was placed beneath the hanging privates in the center.

Bedpans were emptied before each shift change. There was little clearance between the sides of the steel frame and the height of the bedpan. Nurse's aides, whose job it was to empty them, often did not warn a patient to pull their "jewels" out of the way, while yanking the bedpan out. During the day, patients alert enough lifted themselves. But those who could feel and were still unable to control their flow, or who were asleep, could be heard screaming with the pinch in the middle of the night.

"Motherfucker! At least give me a fucking warning!"

Lloyd's infections cleared, and in spite of the loss of blood he had "donated" to the insects at night, he was actually gaining weight. Upon admission, he'd weighed in at a scrawny 65 pounds. After six months, he had already gained eleven pounds owing to the gradual eradication of infection that had slowed his metabolism and allowed badly needed weight gain.

Yack had surgery on his feet, and he was gaining weight as well. It wasn't long before he was released from isolation and joined the other boys in Ward 14. Lloyd felt sad that day.

Lloyd felt sad the day Yack was released from isolation.

Yack tried to console him. "Don't worry, Ace. I'll come roun' to see ya."

And he did occasionally, but it wasn't the same. Yack would only stop by for a couple of minutes then return to the main ward. Lloyd had to spend another six months in isolation, and it seemed as though it was two years.

Christmas approached and the kids bantered over who would be furloughed and who would have to remain at E-town. As Lloyd was still in isolation and without visiting family, there was little doubt that he would be among those who would have to stay at the hospital for the holidays.

He grew increasingly depressed as Wards 14 and 16 emptied and the place quieted to almost monastic solitude.

The nurses became more attentive. Since Lloyd was alone and in isolation however, they tried to spend as much time with him as they could. They even allowed him to stay up all night on Christmas Eve if he chose. But they weren't family, and Lloyd was so tired he could barely keep his eyes open.

That night of December 24, 1965, Lloyd watched TV as long as he could. At approximately 2:00 AM he was laying there depressed, looking out the window at the soft falling snow, when one of the night nurses sauntered over. He didn't recognize her. She was a fill-in for the regular night shift.

Easily 200 plus pounds, and at least 60 years old, the few teeth she had were yellow and gnarled. Her uniform was wrinkled, but clean, and she smelled like heaven to him. She had very little hair, and she waddled much like Mrs. Gipe.

With labored breath, she slowly grabbed a chair and moved it next to Lloyd's bed. In the process of planting herself, she had to stabilize the chair to keep from falling. With her back to him, she grabbed it with both hands as though she were on the high seas and had to negotiate rolling waves. Once she was certain the chair was anchored, she stopped all motion just long enough to gather her next breath.

Lloyd studied her backside as she held herself suspended above the chair, wondering what it was that prevented her from casually placing her torso down in the seat. As though poked by a cattle prod, she spun her entire body in a perfect 180 degrees, and planting herself firmly into position, sat squarely in front of him. He was amazed at how adept she was for someone so obviously out of shape. Once planted, the seat of the chair disappeared, but with adroit gyration, the chair never moved.

Lloyd eyed her as she gathered herself. Her legs were thick, and her uniform was so tight it was as though without it, her entire epidermis would spill out over the chair.

"Merry Christmas," he said in a somber voice.

She needed time to catch her breath. "How... are you... Lloydie?"

As he looked at her. His ears belied his vision. The unseemly embodiment of this woman was only a distraction of the senses. Once she spoke in a voice so soft and melodic, she struck a nerve deep inside of him, so much so, he could hardly hold back the tears. She picked up on his pain and touched his arm. "You don't have to feel bad. I'll stay with you."

His emotions began to spill out and he wept openly. "I just don't understand why my family doesn't want to see me."

The woman may have had many reasons to be angry, although she was wise enough to know that expressing such anger to him would do much more harm than good. "Try not to be too hard on them. They probably have a lot on their plate right now and don't appreciate what a sweet child they have in you."

"I just don't understand why my family doesn't want to see me."

Her words and especially the sound of her voice comforted Lloyd and he began to settle. "I don't think they love me anymore."

His words likely pained her. She had heard them from too many patients. The nursing staff was acutely aware of which patients had attentive families. Lloyd could sense her disapproval by the way she gritted her teeth.

"I'm sure they love you. People have a strange way of showing their love."

"They say I'm too much of a burden on them."

"Someday they'll feel sorry how badly they treated you. You'll get through this time before you know it. Don't fret." With that, she reached out and held his hand lightly.

With her frayed, overweight, and motley look, she was the most beautiful woman in the world to Lloyd that night. Her angelic voice soothed him and her empathy calmed his abject depression. He even wanted to make love to her.

She picked up on his overactive libido and, without discomfort, sidestepped that issue. He felt comforted and soon fell fast asleep. She stayed with him for almost two hours that night.

Parents often abandoned their children at this hospital... and not just around the holidays.

This scene was common. Parents often abandoned their children, and not just around the holidays, dropping them off upon admission and not seeing them until their discharge. Her notes in the medical charts reflected concern about many of the patients that night. She knew the families had no real excuse. A simple card, if only a note or a phone call to the nursing station, would have brightened the days of many of the kids.

There were a few patients with families that remained in touch, some receiving mail every day. Most, however, were left wondering where they fit in the world. Consumed by anger or confusion, just having someone with this nurse's level of empathy alleviated much of the misery of those in her care.

Lloyd never saw the woman again, but was able to get through the remainder of the holiday reasonably unscathed emotionally. That was the first of four Christmases he would spend at E-town, each more rueful than the last.

Shortly after the holidays, Gary Muller was admitted and sent directly into isolation, across from Lloyd. Gary had been in a severe car accident as a teenager, developed infection in one of his injured legs, and needed extensive surgery on his hips. Stocky and overly arrogant, he bragged, "I started shaving when I was 12, on my chest and face."

Although playing his guitar and singing were his only pleasurable traits, Gary felt that shaving was a shortcut to maturity. With curly light brown hair, he was neither well groomed, nor well mannered. His language was deplorable. Verbally abusive to everyone, he even refused to bathe. He liked Lloyd though, and respected him.

Gary would play his guitar and he and Lloyd would sing and talk together until lights out. The conversations were very different than those Lloyd had with Yack. Gary needed someone to answer his many questions about life, whereas Yack, having all the answers of the world, rarely asked questions.

Ostracizing the isolation boys was well ingrained in both Wards 14 and 16, so Yack would have to pay a dear price for his power grab, one of which was jettisoning someone who had been his closest ally—Lloyd.

In sparse interactions, it appeared to Lloyd that Yack's attitude toward him was changing. Yack was quick to criticize Lloyd's every move. He wheeled over one evening, positioned his wheelchair inside Lloyd's doorway, leaned on one arm and asked congenially, "Hey Ace, How're ya doin'?"

Lloyd was watching TV, but was always eager to talk. He turned the volume down. "I'm doin' good, man. How 'bout you?"

Yack leaned in and spoke in a low tone. "I don't know how to put it to you, so I'm just gonna throw it out there."

"Okay..."

"You know, Ace, when we were together in isolation, you were cool." Yack paused, rubbing his right hand through his hair. "You're just not cool anymore."

Lloyd had been happy to see Yack, but was now shocked. "What do you mean, I'm not cool anymore?"

"Well, let's face it. You're over here with this asshole, singin' songs and shit. Come on!"

Yack's demeanor was calm. He was doing what Yack had always done, instructing the less informed.

Lloyd, formerly Yack's protégé, was not impressed. "Hey, I like to sing. And Gary's all right. He's got problems, but don't we all?"

"Yeah, well, it's just not cool."

Yack knew they were having fun, and was a little jealous. He had gained ground, but not with all the kids of the big ward. A few of the older ones, Gary Yates for starters, were not fond of Yack's social prowess. Gary Yates felt Yack was vying to usurp his own power in Ward 14.

For someone who previously respected and revered Yack, the comment was a deep blow to Lloyd. For the first time in a long time, Lloyd was beginning to gain confidence, instead of frustrating himself trying to be a carbon copy of someone else. Lloyd had enjoyed the adoration and attention he received from Gary Muller.

His response to Yack was, "Okay, I hear ya. I guess you're fittin' in real good on the ward these days."

"Hey, whattiya mean, 'fittin' in'?"

"You know what I mean. You think yur so cool."

Yack was visibly angry at Lloyd's response. He unlocked his chair and, moving away from the door, pointed at Lloyd. "Be cool, man."

"Yeah, I'll be cool..."

As Yack wheeled away, Lloyd felt the pain of his old friend's criticism, not fully understanding. Lloyd wouldn't dare show it and give Yack the satisfaction though.

He saw glimpses of Yack from afar after that, but felt confident he could do without Yack's further tutelage. Maybe he had learned all he could from Yack. They would face off again, at a later date, and the results would be considerably different.

Amid all of the struggles on the patient, nursing, and administrative levels, there was an ardent maintenance group, dedicated to the cleaning and repair of the building and transport of the patients. These were the people whose tireless efforts helped to maintain a high standard of quality control amid almost insurmountable obstacles, and those with whom Lloyd felt the closest affinity.

The administration maintained a strict policy of hiring older people, especially those working closely with patients. In the mid to late 1960s, however, they began to relax the age policy, insisting younger people had to be hired, but only within rigid disciplines. This wasn't too difficult. Elizabethtown is located in the heart of Amish and Mennonite country. Anyone applying for a job from either of those cultures could guarantee a richly ethical conduct.

Lloyd had just returned from class one morning in the spring of 1966 when a girl in her early 20s came in with a bucket and mop to clean his room. A bit

A girl in her early 20s came in with a bucket and mop to clean his room...

overweight, with splotchy blemishes across her face, her perfume was strong. She was plain looking, with a hair net bun on the very rear of her scalp. She was so quiet she wouldn't even speak when spoken to.

Lloyd was pleased to see a young female cleaning his room. He didn't see that often enough. He attempted to connect with her.

"Good morning."

She only nodded without slowing her cleaning. She was as silent as new-fallen snow on an open meadow as she went about her work. She neither raised her head nor said a word as she methodically mopped the floor and wiped down the porcelain.

Lloyd tried in vain to get her to speak. "How's the weather outside?"

She only shrugged, but smiled as she was forced to acknowledge his futile attempts. She had been schooled that any attempt at communication by the patients was to be rebuffed. She systematically gathered all her equipment and began shuffling out the door.

As she was leaving, Lloyd gave it one last shot. "Thank you so much."

She bowed and silently closed the door behind her. This became the routine for the next few weeks, always the nod and the bow, without a word spoken.

Maggie was 24 and lived with her parents, deeply religious people.

Lloyd found out her name was Margaret, and that people called her Maggie. She was 24 and lived with her parents, deeply religious people, on their farm. Energetic, she worked hard and had applied for the housekeeping position at E-town in spite of her family's objections. They did not want her exposed to outside influences. They also sheltered her because she suffered with epilepsy. She had been hired to clean Wards 14 and 16 only upon the condition that she not fraternize with the patients in any capacity. To someone so pure, fraternizing was as foreign to her as the man in the moon.

Gary spoke to Lloyd about her the first night. "Man, she's an ugly som-bitch!"

This was Lloyd's first indication of how insensitive Gary could be.

Gary laid it on thick. "I wouldn't touch that with a 10-foot pole!"

Lloyd tried to defend her. "She may be plain looking, but she's a woman!"

Lloyd couldn't dissuade Gary from making fun of her. He even encouraged it a bit to keep Maggie his exclusive domain, though he held no such right.

With each day that Maggie cleaned, Lloyd continued to badger her more, while learning a valuable lesson about relationships. *Redirect the conversation from yourself and center it on those you wish to get closest to.*

"Is your name Margaret?"

Quietly, almost indiscernible, she said, "Most people call me Maggie."

"You have a net on your head. Is that to keep your hair clean?"

Lloyd had seen nurses with their caps and thought it was because they had to keep their hair clean and neatly in place.

Maggie seemed uncomfortable. "I have to wear a covering on my head because I'm Mennonite."

Lloyd was entirely unfamiliar with the discipline. "Is that like Amish?"

She never slowed her pace. Continuing to mop the floor, and without looking up, she said, "It's like it, but a bit different. We're plain people, too."

Lloyd scrambled for something, anything, to encourage conversation. "What does it mean to be 'plain', Maggie?"

"We are instructed by our church to dress plain and live plain. My family does not have a car. Some Mennonites have cars, they're known as 'Black-bumper' Mennonites." This was a person who strictly adhered to church doctrine.

Lloyd had no idea what or who he was dealing with, but with each question, he noticed that she opened up a bit more. "You're very religious, aren't you, Maggie?"

"Yes. We have to study the Bible every day."

Lloyd was so enamored he did whatever he could to keep her talking.

Lloyd was so enamored he did whatever he could to keep her talking, always about herself.

She was unaccustomed to so much attention. Careful to not display her emotions, at no time did she slow her cleaning routine. Once finished, she gathered her things and left abruptly.

Lloyd was dealing with a person whose faith was extremely strict and overbearing, a culture that controlled virtually every aspect of her existence. Sequestered much of her life, Maggie had very few social skills, other than those cultivated within the disciplined lifestyle of her family, immediate friends, and her church. *I must be very careful with this person.*

Lloyd had no idea the internal conflict he was placing this girl under in addressing her the way he did. She had little or no skills with which to answer his questions. She led a cloistered lifestyle. Although she appreciated his attention, leaving without a word was as natural to her as breathing.

This same scenario played itself out over two months. Lloyd wasn't making any noticeable progress. For all his questions, and as hard as he would try, Maggie would not give him anything more than a cursory response. After weeks of exhausting every possible angle, he realized that in order to get closer to Maggie, he would have to learn a lot more about her faith. And he would have to convince her that he was interested in becoming more faithful himself.

There could be little doubt in Maggie's mind how attracted he was to her. She began to respond kindly to him as a result, but only incrementally. Perhaps she was hungry for a little understanding and compassion, both repressed in her world, although she had trouble recognizing either.

Their most spirited communication involved faith and her religion. But if she answered him at all, her work never slowed. She rarely looked up, and when she did, avoided eye contact at all cost.

"Could you teach me about the Bible, Maggie?"

"Well, you have to read it to try to understand."

"Are there any sections that you think I should read?"

"Well, the Four Gospels are good. The New Testament, and Ecclesiastes are good."

Lloyd was given a Bible from one of the staff and started reading it feverishly. As he read something, he would discuss it with Maggie when she came in to clean. She was pleased that he did. As this was an extension of her own faith and teachings, she could continue her work cleaning, and study the Good Book at the same time.

His only interest was to woo her. Whatever he read from the Bible, he constantly put a slight slant on his interpretation to include discussions of relations between a man and a woman. While she appreciated the attention, the first few weeks of this agitated her. She would listen to what he presented but object when his interpretations ranged beyond her belief.

Lloyd was given a Bible and started reading it feverishly. His only interest was to woo Maggie.

Still, Lloyd studied like a maniac. He had to have her and there was only one avenue—through her faith. Finally, after three months, he found this passage and read it to Maggie.

"Ecclesiastes chapter four, verses nine through eleven. Two are better than one, because they have a good return for their labor. If either of them falls down, one can help the other up. But pity anyone who falls and has no one to help them up. Also, if two lie down together, they will keep warm. But how can one keep warm alone?"

He repeated, "...if two lie down together, they will keep warm. But how can one keep warm alone?" with relentless exuberance. Again, she resisted, only this time, there was a slight smile associated with the rebuff, as though she were giving him credit for the try.

In subsequent days, he tried the same argument with minor deviations. Slowly, carefully, over a period of two weeks, he presented her with differing positive arguments for a literal translation of the passage.

His relentless approaches began to open her up. Her work-pace would not slow, but as she started addressing Lloyd more directly, she exhibited a level of empowerment heretofore unseen. Although many times Lloyd felt as though this was merely an exercise in mental banter, he could still sense he was opening avenues of compassion and sensitivity. Each time, all of this occurred within a limited 10-minute period of her cleaning process followed by a hasty departure.

Just prior to her leaving one day, he pleaded, "Maggie, could I please shake your hand?"

She was taken off guard. She knew there should be no contact made with patients, and that to do so could jeopardize her work status. Beyond that, she was not accustomed to physical contact. But it now seemed like she relished the banter and looked forward to her talks with Lloyd.

It started innocently enough...

It started innocently enough. She shook his hand for the first few days as she was leaving the room. By the third day, Lloyd held her hand a little longer. Over time, she allowed him to stroke her hand while she continued to mop the floor near his bed, literally holding the mop with one hand while holding his with the other. Always, any contact was made out of the view of others.

Her pace never slowed. Her sense of detachment was remarkable, so much so that she rarely showed any emotion at all. She would begin her mopping, hold his hand, and as soon as her work was completed, gather all her materials and leave the room without one word spoken.

As days passed, Maggie came in, cleaned areas furthest from his bed first, then those closest to his bed last. Lloyd carried on the conversations, asking her how her day was and the weather outside, always mixing in religion and her faith.

In another month, she approached his bed and extended her hand to hold Lloyd's. As they became more familiar with the routine, now well into its third month, Lloyd gradually reached higher and higher on her arm.

It took weeks before she leaned closer and allowed him to touch her waist. Lloyd thought he would explode! This all had to be done carefully, so as not to offend her sensibilities... and always beyond the view of anyone else, especially the nurses. As soon as someone else came in, or passed by Lloyd's room, Maggie deftly moved to one side and away from his reach.

It took weeks before she leaned closer and allowed him to touch her waist.

Each week Lloyd became bolder and she a bit more conciliatory. Things went well beyond normal boundaries. One day while Lloyd had lazily placed his left arm on the side of the bed, hoping she would reach for his hand, Maggie slowly worked her way over to him. When she did, she grazed his arm with her thigh. He wondered if this was a mere happenstance or could be a sign of another, deeper stage in their relationship.

He was pleasantly surprised when she stepped back to re-mop areas she had already covered and "grazed" him again.

Without any movement on his part, Maggie re-stroked her thigh and moved to position her buttocks against his arm.

Lloyd was in a state of total euphoria. He couldn't believe that after so much time, his relentless approach to her was finally paying off. His left arm transformed from a mere appendage to a raw nerve. Every inch of skin on that arm erupted in an explosion of delight.

> *Lloyd was in a state of total euphoria.*

Frozen in place, he didn't do anything that would at all distract her from her purpose. And he wasn't even sure what that purpose was. Only that, with each intentional movement on her part, she was pleasing him beyond his wildest dreams.

She wore a light-green uniform that extended just beyond her knees. In time, she became more adventurous and rubbed herself against him with greater and more aggressive pressure. It wasn't long before Lloyd began exploring the lower part of her legs and points north. As her "intentional" pressings continued, she encouraged him to explore higher. His immediate discovery was her thick stockings. He was amazed at just how many undergarments a woman of her faith actually wore.

Soon she allowed him complete access underneath her uniform. With her heavy white nylon stockings and a thick corset girdle that ran down both legs to just above her knees, having the ability to touch her exposed skin was out of the question.

Her advances were much greater than his. Where he would not jeopardize alienating her affections by being too aggressive, there were even times she bent down and allowed access for him to touch the outer garments of her breasts.

He wanted more, but with her Rubenesque form buttressed by heavy fabric, Maggie's outer garments were almost all he could bear. Despite the fact that he could not touch any part of her secretive flesh, gaining access beneath her skirt served him nicely. It was all very affectionate and performed with the utmost respect. They loved each other and would get the chance to re-ignite their passion at a later date.

With the eradication of infection, Lloyd's wounds were healing with remarkable progression. He would soon be released from isolation to join the others in the main Ward 14. This was not an altogether new experience for him. He had lived in a ward with other guys before at Kessler Institute in New Jersey. It would take some adjustment though. He would no longer have the freedoms he enjoyed in isolation. He wouldn't be able to stay up as late as he wanted, and would have to negotiate with other kids to watch his favorite programs on TV.

In the fall of 1966, Lloyd, like millions, was a "Trekkie." Lights-out was 8:30 PM and Star Trek ran from 8:30-9:30 PM While in isolation, he found ways to watch it without tipping off the nurses. After all the lights were turned out and the nurses closed Lloyd's door, he quietly pulled his television closer to his bed and, dimming the brightness and turning the sound down, he watched the entire show without being seen.

He would soon be released from isolation...

E-town hospital is situated in a deep valley. When storms rolled from the west or south, they came to a veritable halt when they hit the cavernous Elizabethtown area of Lancaster County, Pennsylvania. The volume of the thunder and lightning strikes were off the dial. The sound shook every heavy block of the old institution.

On one of his remaining nights in isolation, there was a monstrous storm. When lightning struck, the entire building lit up.

Lloyd was angry. He hadn't seen his family in almost two years. He was beginning to think there was no way out of this hospital, and now they were moving him to the main ward with no privacy... and no further contact with Maggie.

As the rolling thunder of the approaching storm grew, he opened his windows, stuck his head out and screamed, "Fuck you, God! *Fuck you!*"

As the words passed his lips, a streak of blinding light struck a tree less than twenty feet from his window. Wood splintered and splattered against the outside screen. His world went black. The energy shook Lloyd to his core and almost threw him out of bed. His immediate thought was the awesome *power of the Lord!* He recovered though. His sight returned and he was left a shaking glob of frenzied nerves. After that, he developed reverence and a much deeper respect for the powers of Mother Nature.

Lloyd was released from isolation shortly thereafter, but although free, the ward had its own even greater restrictions. With his sacrifice of privacy, he knew his relationship with Maggie would have to be curtailed... and that was his most consuming grief of all.

EIGHT

WARD 14

*People appreciate rewards in equal measure
to the depths of adversity they've endured.*

The ward was a marked departure from isolation. The first thing sacrificed for Lloyd was privacy. Since there were twenty people, ten to a side, finding refuge from spying eyes was a full-time job.

The group quickly pounced upon adverse remarks or hysterical movements made by weaker members. If you were tough, you had far more freedom to express yourself, since people did not fool with those they thought could explode and inflict harm.

There were also discussions regarding differences between those born with physical maladies and those whose similar disability was incurred as a traumatic event. Those born with their condition adapted with greater ease. Much as someone born with only three fingers on each hand, they do not miss that which they never had.

Patients felt "free" through as small a gesture as removing an arm cast, or the removal of leg pins months after surgery. For patients with curvature of the spine, freedom was felt when the body cast was taken off leading up to and following a spine-fusing operation. Some celebrated their freedom with the ability to use a stretcher, wheelchair, or crutches versus being confined to bed.

Stretchers were Lloyd's main mode of transportation at the time. These were a stripped down version of their modern counterpart. A lighter form of a movable bed, they had no side-rails, no IV pole holes or connections, and no ability to elevate the upper or lower section. It was a flat, stainless steel plate with a thick hard-rubber bumper encircling the upper platform. A patient rested four feet off the floor on a rubber-coated foam mat, covered with a thin cotton draw sheet, all on top of four galvanized wheels with hard-rubber tires. The deluxe model had a thin stainless steel plate below the resting platform, just above the height of the tires, used to store things.

Well oiled, the stretchers moved gracefully. Patients, lying on their stomachs, quickly learned how to push themselves off walls, doors, bedposts, or anything with the slightest stability (even people), to propel themselves to their desired destinations. The downside to self-propulsion was that if the patient leaned too far over one side, the wheels could buckle under the carriage, overturning and dumping them onto the floor. Lloyd learned that lesson the hard way.

Already a year and a half into his stay, Lloyd's greatest freedom was being released from isolation into the main ward. With his popularity growing, obtaining a modicum of control was an interesting concept. For the first time in his life he actually felt as though he was gaining the ability to commandeer his own destiny.

He had no family to oversee his care, and there was clear evidence, even to those less observant, that powerful hospital administrators were losing in their attempts to ameliorate the frustration of the kids. This observation was not lost on the patients or lower-level staff.

Lloyd's newfound confidence was not unique. As the number of self-assured patients increased, so did the number of commensurate incidents of those challenging authority. The power held over the patients by the staff was waning, and it scared the staff keen enough to recognize it.

Ward 14 was a large rectangular room, fifty feet long by twenty-five feet wide. The ceiling was fifteen feet high, from which hung six fluorescent lamps from five-foot poles, three on each side of the ward. The patients dubbed these as the "spotlights" or "spots." They were spread evenly throughout the ward to scatter blinding light to every corner.

There were six switches on the wall closest to the nursing station, corresponding to each of the massive fluorescents. Nurses carried flashlights, but when they forgot or hadn't replaced the batteries, they did not hesitate to turn on the "spotlights" to see what they needed to complete their tasks. And, when they turned them on, they weren't selective about the switches they threw. Many times, the blinding effects of the lights intended for one patient woke everyone.

A single bed was pushed tight against each of the four corners of the elongated space. The other beds were side by side in twos, arranged ten to a side, and separated with only a narrow metal wall. The two beds within the metal walls with a three-foot separation were designated as a "cubicle." Each patient had his own small metal cabinet alongside his bed, which held a urinal, a bedpan, and his personal items. It wasn't easy to remain aloof from a cubicle mate, but when a patient had nineteen roommates, privacy was always at a premium.

When a patient had nineteen roommates, privacy was always at a premium.

People with critical maladies required more attention by the medical staff. Normal nursing chores included periodic blood pressure and temperature readings, fluid intake/output, and emptying urinals and bedpans.

Awake or asleep, if a patient just didn't want to be bothered, somewhere on the ward a struggle with the staff would ensue. Those lying on their stomachs on a Stryker bed, with their testicles hanging down, could always be heard when "pinched" by the removal of their bedpan.

During the day, noise decibels remained at peak levels. It wasn't uncommon for someone to screech a demand from across the ward rather than pass the message along or wait to speak to someone closer.

At night the sound required one to grow impervious. Some moaned in their sleep with present or former nightmares. Most nights you could hear the muffled chatter of those who, for whatever reason, were unable to fall asleep. Particularly annoying was the intermittent clashing, clumping footsteps of the nursing supervisors as they stomped their way through the ward, all hours of the night, en route to the nurses station and the elevator beyond.

With enough exposure, all become immune to the smells. There was always a multitude of open heavy stainless steel bedpans, full of urine. Someone was always having a stool or laying in excrement. Compound that with one or two people sick to their stomachs, puking their guts out, and dressing changes being done to people with varying stages of infected pressure ulcers, and you had a hodgepodge of ugly sights, sounds, and especially pungent odors.

Everyone in the ward was conditioned by the same routine. At 4:00 AM the night nurse's aides would come into the ward, rolling a small metal cart with stacks of washcloths in basins full of warm water. As they progressed through the ward, they would wring out the washcloths one by one, and thrust them into sleeping hands or directly onto a slumbering face if the individual resisted too adamantly. The aides would then either empty the patient's bed-bag, bedpan, or just have them wash their face and hands, and allow them to fall back to sleep, if they were able.

At 6:55 AM, the kitchen delivered the large food cart to the nurse's station, via the back elevator. The nurses then pushed the huge warming cart into the center of the ward. Made of solid stainless steel, the food cart had six food compartments of varying sizes, each with its own handled metal lid.

Meals were consistent. For breakfast three days each week, containers held powdered eggs, three days oatmeal, and on Saturdays the patients were treated to "shit on the shingle"—creamed dried beef on toast. Lunches consisted mainly of a soup that many complained was created by filling a pot with water splashed over a chicken, and simple bologna sandwiches. Dinners were instant potatoes, frozen peas and carrots, and veal patties during the week, and frozen fish sticks on Fridays. White bread and margarine were plentiful. Whatever could be frozen or powdered was the consistent fare.

On Saturdays patients were treated to "shit on the shingle" — creamed dried beef on toast.

At precisely 7:00 AM when she was on, Mrs. Gipe honored the patients by pulling her long stainless steel serving spoon out, and wielding it like a mallet for a big bass drum. She wailed it on the side of the metal cart, her idea of a tribal wake up call.

Wham! Wham! Wham!

"Wake up, sleepyheads, and git yur breakfast!"

Surveying the entire ward, she made sure that all were awake before serving.

"Nobody eats 'til yur all up. *Wake up!*"

The screech of her voice could penetrate well beyond multiple layers of blankets and pillows. She was relentless in her efforts to stimulate movement in the unconscious bodies. She continued her drumbeat.

Wham! Wham! Wham!

The effect of metal against metal was ear shattering, a sound so high on the treble scale as to cause pain to dogs in the next county.

A smattering of moans could be heard over the fading wail.

"So help me, Gary Tates, if you don't wake up, I'll throw a bucket o' cold water on you!"

"Fuck you, bitch!"

With that she trundled off to the nurse's station in a huff, leaving the cart in place. Those still too novice to understand thought she had given up in defeat. Most of the nurses didn't fool with Gary, at least that early in the morning.

Just as patients were lulled into another restful snooze, Mrs. Gipe appeared in the doorway again, this time heading full steam toward Gary's bed, bucket in hand.

Swoosh!

The entire contents of the bucket of cold water hit him square in the face and torso. Gary sprang up and shouted a ream of epithets that ran afoul of everything foul. "You fucking, ugly whore..."

He continued for the next thirty minutes, but wide-awake. She paid no mind. Casually turning, she left the room and returned with another bucket of even colder water she dispensed on him as well. Though her underlings motioned to change his bed, Mrs. Gipe ordered that Gary lay in the wet for the duration of the shift.

Very little could dispel the deep anger Gary nurtured. He was Mrs. Gipe's special target, and she used her own brand of psychological weaponry on him. It was more of an abject lesson she imparted for the benefit of the rest of the group, although after the prolonged frustration many had to deal with, abject lessons began to fade as well.

Days were spent in a maddening state of flux. Twice a week, following breakfast, doctors performed their rounds. A group of four doctors (usually residents on their orthopedic rotation), followed by a few of the ward nurses—Mrs. Gipe and Miss Laux, and the Director of Nursing—would ease their way through the ward, performing a cursory evaluation. Only a short introduction and small talk would involve the patient. Requests or questions were summarily squelched by the nursing staff or, more specifically, Miss Laux. Only those patients freshly placed in the ward would dare breech her etiquette. Much like a passing rain cloud, normal activities of the day would begin in the wake of this superficial evaluation, bathing, dressing, and preparation for transport to school.

Crowded in small 9' by 12' space from 9:00 AM 'til noon, patients in beds and stretchers were lined up like sardines on one side, with people in wheelchairs and on crutches scattered randomly. Boys and girls of varying ages and levels of knowledge were taught together, each at his or her own level of progression.

Lloyd's teacher was Miss Oberholtzer. Miss Oberholtzer was crippled with severe degenerative arthritis and suffered the pain associated with it silently. She stood tall at only 4'10", had thick arms she hung at her sides, and legs that only allowed her a slow uneven gait. She walked with a side-to-side movement in a sort of duck waddle, as though locked at the hips. Her fingers were so gnarled and stiff she could barely grasp or point. Her hair, thick and black, was cut in a bowl shape, with short bangs that hung straight down, framing a puffy red face.

Her eyes were piercing, and once her ire was up, she could freeze a subject in place while she ridiculed them to a pulp. Well educated and highly intelligent, no comment escaped her and no one could outsmart her.

Miss Oberholtzer accepted few excuses, least of which were ones associated with a disability.

Miss Oberholtzer held strict adherence to quiet in her classroom, with the peace broken only by her intermittent chastising of someone who refused to do as instructed or who failed to grasp the material. She accepted few excuses, least of which were ones associated with a disability. She had no time for whining or crybabies. Though anyone speaking out of turn or trying anything untoward was severely rebuked, she would occasionally announce a break by pointing to something in nature out the window, explaining her knowledge of the subject or breaking out in uncontrollable laughter, referring to her beloved newspaper cartoon strip "Peanuts" and what Lucy had in store for Charlie Brown that day.

One teacher in each of two older-age classrooms taught rudimentary subjects closest to the "3 R's"—reading, writing, and 'rithmetic—and only a passing knowledge of science, usually biology. At noon, patients were then returned to the ward for midday lunch. At 1:00 PM, they were moved back to the classroom for two more hours of instruction. After school, they were transported to the physical therapy department for two hours and back to the ward at 5:00 PM when dinner was served promptly.

Medications and therapy took priority over every other activity. Even if patients were not on the ward, nurses sought them out to administer medications. It was not uncommon to see the nursing staff enter a classroom to empty necessary drainage bags, bedpans, or take blood pressures, temperature readings and such.

From 5:00 to 8:00 PM, patients roamed about the ward and were pretty much on their own (within prescribed boundaries and standards of conduct, of course) to do as they pleased without much supervision. At 8:00 PM patients were required to be back in bed for lights out at 8:30.

As would be expected, the time between dinner and bedtime was the freest and most potentially destructive. Those able on the boy's ward would move to the playroom, as far from supervision as possible, and throw baseball cards or engage in a lively group of poker. This is how many of the boys amassed the small fortunes they were able to trade for clothes or food brought from home.

This is also how those more devious created plans of their own.

NINE

BARNEY AND THE LAW

"Sometimes we make things too easy, and rescue failure."
—Renate Blaschek

His first few days on the ward were spent alone and vulnerable. Lloyd knew only a smattering of the kids, and of those, only by name. The ones he didn't know looked at him with disdain and mistrust, someone else to "break in." Yack acknowledged Lloyd, but kept his distance. After their last meeting, apparently he wanted Lloyd to either sink or swim in his newfound environment.

Lloyd wasn't given an aptitude test. The powers that be just accepted that when he said he was in ninth grade, he was telling the truth. After all, they had Miss Oberholtzer to evaluate that. Now that he was out in the ward, Lloyd had been issued some schoolbooks corresponding to his perceived ability. He would attend class with the rest of the kids, so without camaraderie on the ward, he turned to his schoolbooks for solace.

Living in tight quarters with nineteen people was tough enough; bunking next to Barney Tanicki was a lesson in diplomacy. Barney had sustained burns over eighty percent of his body from a house fire. He had severe brain damage and the loss of one leg just above the knee. At age 14, and with diminished mental capacity, his family, who had abandoned him long before his admission to E-town, was only a fleeting memory.

Barney was Lloyd's first cubicle-mate. He was calm unless taunted by other kids, and with his inability to understand clearly, an easy target for the crueler members of the clan. Once assaulted, Barney would attack with whatever object he was holding. Lloyd took it as his personal responsibility to temper Barney's rage whenever possible. What Lloyd was not aware of was that Barney's frustration could smolder, sometimes for days, before he would explode.

Joel Hooker, who was in the bed opposite Lloyd's, had been born with deformities to both of his feet. Standing 5'8" and lanky, Joel had surgery and had casts below his knees to the tips of both feet. Doctors felt that plastering was an effective way to regenerate viable tissue. It presumably immobilized the affected area and provided an enclosed cocoon to promote healing.

A week after the surgery, the doctor ordered the placement of walking-heels—three-inch rubber soles—on both feet of Joel's casts. With the use of crutches, he now had the ability to get out of bed, go to the bathroom, and move about, a freedom few in the ward could enjoy. Highly intelligent and with a keen, dry wit, Joel could be cruel to those with lesser intelligence, and his mouth got him into trouble. Joel, more the cerebral type, didn't fight too effectively. When kids picked on him, however, he was highly adept at throwing things at them as they tried to get away.

Lloyd was minding his own business one evening, reading a schoolbook, when Joel started in on him. "Hey, what's your name?"

"Lloyd."

"No. Your last name, dipshit! What's your last name?"

Lloyd could sense where this was going, but played along. "Negoescu."

"What? Nee-bo, Nee-oski, Nee-fuck, what de fuck?"

Other kids began to laugh. Lloyd wondered if he would have to kick this kid's ass. Calmly he said, "Neg-o-es-cu."

Joel kept pressing, and the contagion of laughter behind him from the other patients, one of which was Yack, was wearing Lloyd thin.

"No. Let's just call you Nee-bo-scum!"

A loud clamor came from the group. With a steely glare Lloyd said, "How 'bout we don't, before you get your ass kicked?"

Joel didn't back down. "Ooooooh, I'm shakin' in my boots. You're not so tough. I heard about you gettin' your ass kicked by Sparks. You're not in isolation anymore and can't hide in your little room!"

Lloyd just stared at him and said, "I won't hide from you, Joel..."

Now, others chimed in. "Oooooooh..."

Lloyd just turned and continued to read his book.

He wasn't sure he could kick Joel's ass, and it scared him to think about it. He only knew that there was a law within this group that dictated that if you backed down or showed weakness of any kind, you lost "face" and instantly became a victim to unspeakable cruelties. Any exhibition of vulnerability made you the prey of lesser vultures you didn't even know. Once word got out that you backed down, you found yourself a target for every creep trying to make his own level of "cred."

If you backed down or showed weakness, you lost "face" and became victim to unspeakable cruelties.

Most of these cruelties were not borne out of necessity. Many were created in the undisciplined minds of people who lived more in their thoughts than their bodies. Win or lose, it didn't matter. With the pain most patients already tolerated just to survive, getting beat up by an opponent was much less of a price to pay for maintaining "face."

All external activities (outside the ward, school, therapy, and so on) were curtailed over the weekends. With more kids going home on weekend furloughs, the nursing staff was reduced as well. One weekend afternoon, while everyone was lounging around, a kid started arguing with Joel over a game they were playing. Most fights started that way. He slapped Joel hard on his face. The kid then turned his wheelchair sharply and bolted away. Joel, who couldn't jump up and catch him with his casts on, casually grabbed one of his crutches. The kid who had slapped him sprinted away like a fleeing bandit. Holding the crutch back in javelin-throwing mode, Joel tossed it like a spear, hitting the kid fifteen feet away, with pinpoint accuracy, right in the back of the head. The kid's wheelchair veered hard to the left and smashed head-on into a bed. He was dazed, but gathered himself after the crash. Lloyd recognized that Joel was not someone to trifle with.

Joel's favorite target for abuse was Barney. He had badgered the boy for days, with minor skirmishes as a result. His tactic was to tease him, and when Barney ran over and started to swing at him, Joel was quick to call the nurses. "Hey, the fuckin' retard is attacking me again! Get him the fuck offa me!"

On a cold May morning in 1966, Lloyd was tossing, trying to catch an extra wink after the four o'clock washcloth slap in the face. The overhead lights were on, which meant that the nurses either had a minor emergency to deal with or that it was nearing breakfast time. Most of the guys were still half asleep, including Joel.

Barney was not held under strict surveillance, so no one noticed when he awoke that morning holding a knife. He was not allowed sharp objects of any kind. Lloyd had become more observant of him since Barney had been coaxed by Joel to attack Lloyd.

Joel would repeat to Barney, "Barney, Lloyd bad, Lloyd bad. Hit him! Hit Lloyd!"

Lloyd knew Barney had no logical way to judge whether what Joel was telling him was true. He acted on whatever anyone told him to do... anyone he knew, that is. So, naturally without warning, Barney had started pouncing on Lloyd. Lloyd would get hit a few times, but finally deflect the blows and restrain Barney long enough to reassure him. This happened a few times before Lloyd turned to Joel, while still holding Barney and said, "The next time you tease him to hit anyone, I'm gonna hit you!" That stopped Joel's targeting of Lloyd.

Since Lloyd had already been on guard, that cold early morning when Barney jumped out of his bed swinging something shiny, headed toward Joel, Lloyd sat straight up and screamed, "Joel, watch out!"

Barney jumped on top of Joel and started stabbing him with ferocity.

Barney jumped on top of Joel and started stabbing him with such ferocity Joel was taken by complete surprise. Unable to respond at first, Joel clumsily leapt up, trying to deflect the blows, but eventually threw his blanket over Barney's head.

The two wrestled violently, Joel screaming for help, Barney continuing his onslaught until nurses pulled him off. Those patients who were conscious enough to understand what was happening cheered.

Joel, shaken, had a few cuts, but was all right. Barney was not removed from the ward, but had his tranquilizers increased. Joel's teasing of Barney stopped. Although he occasionally pushed away some of the guys who desired to tease Barney into hysteria, Lloyd would end up bearing the brunt of Barney's wrath again.

Lloyd's bunk was nearest the large window of the nurse's station, which was extremely annoying. The window had no curtain and there was never a moment, day or night, when the nurses turned off their station lights. Lloyd complained that he was unable to get adequate sleep, but his pleas fell on deaf ears.

Though he had only been on the ward a few weeks, he became a calming force on the other boys, which was not lost on Mrs. Gipe. She finally acquiesced and had his bed moved to another position.

After months of trying, Yack hadn't made that much progress winning over cohorts. With tensions among patients running high, he always seemed to aggravate issues even further. Every time someone would start swearing or throw something, Yack would yell, "Give 'em hell!" "That's it!" or "Go ahead!"

Lloyd's method was less confrontational. In whispers, he quietly defended whatever issue was brewing to whomever was listening. "You know, he probably wouldn't be throwing things if you'd just talk to him a little!"

Defending issues got Lloyd into more trouble than Yack's provocative prodding. Where Yack's aggression could be dismissed, Lloyd's was harder to ignore. This time the nurses were not pleased. Mrs. Gipe would point a finger in Lloyd's direction and say, "Mind yur own bidness, mister!"

Although Lloyd's mouth got him into trouble with administration, he acquired admiration from the most vulnerable of the boys.

While his bed position was moved from the nurse's viewing window to the center of the ward, his bed type was also changed. Now Lloyd was placed on a Stryker turning-frame bed, usually used for orthopedic surgeries, burn victims, or people who remain immobilized but required frequent turning for circulation or to avoid pressure areas. Once the patient is sandwiched between the two canvas-covered platforms, with openings for bedpan and foot placement, the platforms could be screwed tightly on each end, then rotated side to side to flip the patient from face down to lying on his back.

Besides the obvious discomfort of being suspended on a flat piece of canvas, with penis and testicles hanging fully exposed, Lloyd needed to learn to wrap his arms in the sheets at night to prevent them from falling off the side. Often, he tucked his hands under his torso, but with normal sleeping movement, his arms always released and flopped to one side, straining the muscles in his shoulders.

Although his mouth got him in trouble with administration, he acquired admiration from the most vulnerable of the boys. This was an unpopular stance because the more hardened members of the tribe preferred to subjugate the weakest. While others exerted force with wanton cruelty, Lloyd was stealthy. He likened himself to Robin Hood, defending the weak, but in the process, exacting cruelties of his own. If he noticed someone beating up on someone much smaller, he would call out for the guy to stop. In the beginning, the abuser would look over at Lloyd, then laugh and continue. Since Lloyd couldn't jump out of bed and he wasn't one to pick up things and start throwing, he just pointed at them and said, "I owe you, pal!"

One morning as George pushed Lloyd's stretcher to class, Lloyd could see one of the abusers approaching from the opposite direction in a wheelchair. This was a tough kid from south Philly who would be discharged soon. George was traveling at a pretty good clip. As they neared each other, grabbing the sides of his stretcher with both hands, Lloyd leaned over to one side and threw his body in the opposite direction, forcing his stretcher right at the kid. The kid veered to avoid the hit, hands on each wheel of his wheelchair. As he did, Lloyd swung and clapped him hard on the side of his head.

Wham!

The smash almost knocked the kid out of his chair. He cried out, "Hey!" but Lloyd and George were now too far beyond him to be implicated. George just smiled. He often witnessed scuffles between patients and turned his back, not wanting to get involved.

The kid was more respectful to Lloyd after that. He figured that someday, someway, Lloyd could settle a score. Word got around that he almost took the kid's eye out. Lloyd's response was, "Hey, I could've closed my fist!"

Lloyd's only physical therapy was lifting weights. His arms had been so thin back when he was in the isolation ward, the physical therapists started him lifting five-pound dumbbells. He lifted as often as he could. He soon found that he was doing 25 to 30 repetition curls for bicep development. When he reached the 30-repetition mark, the therapist increased his weights another five pounds. He learned that if his arm was extended and he rolled the dumbbell out to the tips of his fingers and back again, he could tone his forearms as well. By the time he entered the ward his arms were developing nicely.

Another of the many ways Lloyd commanded respect was his "slap and grab" technique. Since he didn't have the ability to run after anyone, if they showed disrespect to him or someone he liked and they were within grabbing distance, he would slap the person hard on the cheek.

In the beginning, the slap made the person recoil and move away, often requiring further conflict at a later date, as they were out of his reach and regained confidence. With his developed arms and hands, Lloyd learned to slap someone quickly, then grab them and pull them closer. That way, if they thought about escaping, they couldn't. And if they desired to protest, they had every opportunity in his grasp, looking straight into his eyes!

Once a year Hollywood stars visited the hospital as guests from the Shriner's Circus of Philadelphia. Patients were always impressed to see Clayton Moore, The Lone Ranger, and David Canary of Bonanza's "Candy" or whoever was the current holder of the Miss Universe crown walking the halls. For those fortunate enough to be able to attend the circus, it was a real treat, but older teens refused to go. It was a macho thing, as though a circus was only meant for kids. Lloyd never had the option. Barney did though.

It was a hot June day when Barney entered the ward with his cane. Fresh from the Shriner's circus, he was hopping on one leg while swinging his stiff prosthesis, laughing and carrying a balloon.

Lloyd, lying on his stomach on his Stryker bed, had a group of guys engrossed in a profitable game of poker at his bedside. Barney showed off his balloon and Lloyd was only too willing to diffuse his happiness to make himself look more superior.

Lloyd reached over and grabbed the balloon. "Hey, whattaya got there, Barney?"

Barney immediately displayed his outrage. He reached over three people to yank the balloon back with force. Then he swung at Lloyd, barely grazing a shoulder. The poker game came to an abrupt halt when Lloyd grabbed Barney and held him long enough to calm him down.

After a short period, the guys laughingly returned to the game. Barney took his balloon, shook his fist at Lloyd, and walked over to his bed muttering, "Bad Lloyd! Bad!"

No one noticed when Barney snuck up behind, raised his cane by the tip and slammed the handle hard on the center of Lloyd's back.

Whack!

The blow took Lloyd by surprise and he was momentarily incapacitated. Barney swung his cane madly. Everyone scattered. By the third blow, Lloyd was just conscious enough to block subsequent swings and wrest the cane from Barney's grip.

Though Lloyd had his opponent's weapon, Barney was still angry enough to pummel him with both fists. Lloyd wrapped his arms around the boy and held him long enough to immobilize and subdue him.

The nurses ran to assist, but the damage had been done. Barney's swats sprained Lloyd's spine and left welts across his back.

Lloyd learned a lesson that day—he learned not to fool with Barney. Other lessons involving respect for personal property, power, and the corruptible aspects of control would have to be learned later at a much greater cost.

On the ward, the weakest was singled out by the most sadistic, teased until he started to retaliate, then jumped by the teaser and pummeled into submission. The stronger among them, however, were always intimidated by the more intelligent, no matter the difference in size. It was rare to find brawn and brains in the same package. The physically strongest people on the ward in the summer of 1966 were part of Lloyd's crew and some of the kindest people he had ever known.

Lloyd learned a lesson that day... not to fool with Barney.

Patients learned early on not to expect to find refuge with the nursing staff. Other than trying to keep them fed, clothed, warm, and clean, nurses had little time left for protection, let alone discipline. Unless staff was standing right there, they were always too late to intercede, and that was by design.

For reasons far too many to mention, there were times when staff was present during struggles yet decided it best to stand back and let the skirmish finish on its own. The patients were left to their own devices for protection, and they knew it.

Lloyd absorbed this reality, soaking it in like a sponge, and doled out vicious cold-blooded cruelty with impunity like the worst of them.

Angry? You're damned right they were angry!

There were two types of patients: the acutely ill who were more peaceful and pliable (because they were literally fighting for their lives), and the chronically ill, those whose illnesses were not life-threatening, who were the angriest and much more non-compliant.

The chronically ill had plenty of reason to be non-compliant. They were on a savage medical treadmill. The optimal prognosis for most was the patchwork pain they had to endure from archaic medical practices, only to be returned home to the environment from which all of their conditions originated. Slowly, insidiously, they reached the point of what it means to be "institutionalized."

Merriam-Webster describes *institutionalize* as:

"to accustom (a person) so firmly to the care and supervised routine of an institution as to make incapable of managing a life outside."

Wikipedia describes it as:

"...an activity or set of activities which change an individual or group that were not formerly governed by a set of rules to one which is regulated and standardized. In the United States and most other developed societies, severe restrictions have been placed on the circumstances under which a person may be committed or treated against their will as such actions have been ruled by the United States Supreme Court and other national legislative bodies as a violation of civil rights and/or human rights (see e.g. Connor v. Donaldson). Thus a person is rarely committed against their will and is never committed for an indefinite period of time."

Patients having spent a minimum of six months in the Children's Hospital institution showed marked changes in behavior. Although it can be argued whether they had been committed "against their will" because of their age, clearly they were "...lacking the will or ability to think and act independently." Most suffered from "...an activity or set of activities which change an individual or group that were not formerly governed by a set of rules to one which is regulated and standardized." Regulations, if they existed at all, were ambiguous and always imposed at someone else's discretion.

Patients were exposed to activities that were cruel and inhuman on a daily basis. A common refrain was, "Damn, I can't wait to get out of this fucking dump!"

TEN

BOB AND THE THIEF

Honor among thieves is, at its best, wrought with respect, at its least, wrought with fear.

Mrs. Gipe was very forceful in moving patient beds around the ward, like pawns on a chessboard, to achieve greater harmony. Even minor improvements were proof that she was right in her actions.

Male and female patients, separated by the full length of the building, had their respective playrooms. In order to converse with the girls, male patients either made time during school or therapy sessions, like ships passing in the day, or went down the hall at night (with permission, of course) to meet in the lobby between 6:00 and 8:00 PM.

The lobby consisted of administrative offices, as well as the office of Miss Laux, who made it her special mission to prevent patients from obtaining any level of intimacy. For those confined to a bed, making it to the lobby later in the day was out of the question.

Patients physically able to get out of bed could meet their girlfriend without permission, but only by stealth maneuver after "lights out" and under the cover of darkness. It wasn't uncommon to see someone crawling under the beds after hours to meet their girlfriend, or even to simply smack someone in their sleep who had harmed them earlier.

Often a patient would return from physical therapy or school to find his personal cabinet and bed in a completely new position without rhyme or reason. With each move came a new cubicle mate. Rarely, you teamed up with someone who was the perfect match. One such blessing came to Lloyd in the form of Bob Walters.

Deep into summer, the weather was hot with numerous violent thunderstorms. There was no air-conditioning, so the tall glass doors leading to the porches and balconies were always kept open. During the worst storms, lightning streaked through the ward as explosions from thunder enveloped the entire building. Even with lights out, few could sleep under such tumultuous conditions.

Bob's legs were his trouble—a congenital problem he'd dealt with all his life. They were withered and deformed. His arms and chest were a much different story. He stood 5'6", with rugged good looks and upper body strength honed from hard work and a tough life growing up on a farm.

Bob rarely sat in a chair the normal way. He always turned and straddled it to display his strong arms on the chair back. Understandably reserved and quiet, Bob was not only honest but very insightful. He had few illusions. Different from so many, Bob held a mature realism far beyond his years.

The storm outside was raging. Left in abject darkness, the flashes of lightning were blinding. The rumbling thunder was so deafening it was a challenge for patients to even carry on a conversation. However, in his attempt to break the ice, Lloyd leaned over toward Bob. "We had bad storms where I grew up in Jersey."

"Hmm?" Bob nodded, but was unimpressed.

Lloyd thought maybe his cubicle mate just didn't hear him, so he tried again. "I just remember bad storms when I was young."

Bob opened up. "We had bad storms where I live."

"Where's that?"

"West of Pittsburgh... the sticks."

Bob, with his well-defined biceps and forearms, was a mystery to Lloyd. He had a low, slow quiet drawl that was pleasing to the ear. Despite his well-developed stature, he was never threatening to Lloyd and even showed deep respect, as though he perceived they were on the same physical level.

"How'd you get such big arms, man?"

"Liftin' bales."

The familiarity was comforting to Lloyd. Lloyd's family worked a farm when he was young and he could remember his father's powerful arms. "I grew up on a farm myself. It was a great life."

"It's a hard life." Lloyd nodded and Bob continued. "You don't get a vacation. Livestock have to be watered and fed. Cows need milkin' twice a day." He sat up and breathed deeply in exasperation. "Stayin' here's a vacation…"

Lloyd couldn't disagree more. "You haven't been here that long. Give it a chance, the place grows on ya… like a fungus."

Bob laughed. "It can't be. The food's not bad."

Before Lloyd could fill in any further details, Bob asked, "How long you been here?"

"Since February '65."

"Wow… what de hell happened to ya?"

"I was shot in the back by my brother when I was nine."

Bob showed no surprise. "Did he mean to?"

"Kinda. His head was fucked up… still is."

"Sounds rough."

Lloyd laid his head down and Bob didn't push. There was nothing left for either to say, so they both drifted off to sleep.

There were a few robberies on the ward. People complained to the nursing staff that someone was pilfering their stuff, like money, jewelry, baseball cards, and comic books. The smart kids always carried their most prized possessions with them, but the longer you were there, the harder it was to carry everything you had accumulated. Yet nobody of power had anything taken.

Everyone woke early one morning to Stuart Margolies screaming his head off. "Somebody stole my St. Christopher medal!" He started crying uncontrollably. "My mother gave it to me for good luck!"

Few in the ward paid much attention to Stuart. Since he was put in a body cast for curvature of the spine within weeks of his admission, he was considered a "fast tracker" rather than a "lifer," like those who stayed longer than a year and whose families weren't advocating for a speedy return home. Fast trackers were usually at E-town no longer than six to eight months.

Needless to say, lifers weren't too keen on the likes of the Stuarts of the ward, but when someone stole his medal, most felt something had to be done.

Lloyd hadn't been hit by the thief, but if he didn't address the problem, he felt he could shortly become a target. That made him feel vulnerable, and he didn't like that.

Yack, who had begun to feel his influence ebb, couldn't care less about someone else's problems. He had enough of his own to worry about. In an effort to regain lost ground in the ward's power base, he decided to pick a fight with Lloyd.

Lloyd was lying on his framed Stryker bed doing homework shortly after dinner. Bob had just gone to the bathroom and the ward was quiet when Yack came up to him and started talkin' trash. "What'ya up to, bookworm?"

Yack couldn't care less about someone else's problems. He had enough of his own to worry about.

The nickname didn't bother Lloyd. Joel had already branded him "Nebo-Scum," which was shortened to "Scum," and Lloyd joked proudly that it was spelled with two m's, "Scumm," as though that made a difference. He was also sometimes called "nose" for his over-arching proboscis.

But now Lloyd was being challenged by his greatest nemesis. Yack had no use for "bookreadin'." Books were only meant for "the pencil-necked geeks of the world." He resented anyone well read, especially someone vying for the position he coveted most in the ward.

Lloyd took it on his shoulder. "Just homework."

Yack moved his wheelchair closer to Lloyd's bed, and as he did, he reached out and pushed Lloyd's pencil.

Lloyd tried to pay no mind. What bothered him was that after the few months Lloyd was on the ward, they hardly passed two words between them.

But each time Lloyd started to write something, Yack reached over and pushed his pencil, causing Lloyd to scratch a bold mark and rip the page.

He let it go and laughed the first couple of times, but since everyone in the ward watched, he couldn't let too much pass. Finally, after the third jab, he'd had enough. "Hey, watch it!"

Lloyd grabbed Yack's arm and pushed it back. Yack reached over, locking his right arm around Lloyd's right. When he got the hold he was looking for, he pulled Lloyd toward him, swinging with his left and just barely scraping Lloyd's head with his fist.

Now Lloyd was pissed. "You fuck!"

With his left arm, Lloyd shoved all his books and papers into Yack's face. That had the effect Lloyd was looking for. Yack was surprised. By the time he threw the debris off and swung at Lloyd again, Lloyd leaned over and coupled his arm around Yack. Lloyd pulled, locking both Yack's arms under his chin. Yack's face was completely exposed.

Lloyd was able to slip his right arm out from under Yack's arms and cocked his elbow, his fist pointed directly at Yack's face. Red as a beet, Yack was sweating profusely and his eyes bulged wide.

Lloyd held his fist high and aimed, ready to strike for what seemed like an eternity, then he thought better of it and pushed

Yack and his wheelchair away from his bed so hard Yack's chair slammed against the opposite side of the cubicle—Bob's bed!

Yack rubbed his right shoulder, but was likely relieved Lloyd hadn't pulled the trigger with his fist. Lloyd felt good, having made his point about who won that battle, a fight long overdue. Plus everyone on the ward had seen what happened. As far as Lloyd was concerned, it defined who was the toughest.

But within a few minutes, Yack shook it off and was already back to trash talkin'. "Now you know who's boss, bookworm!"

"You gotta be shittin' me!" Lloyd snapped back. "You actually believe you won that?"

"Well, you didn't, bookworm!"

Lloyd was pissed. "Anytime you want round two, I'm ready. Next time, I won't pull my punches!"

Yack just lifted his left arm and thrust his middle finger at Lloyd.

The experience taught Lloyd another valuable lesson. He would not make the same mistake again.

The experience taught Lloyd another valuable lesson—you may not get a second chance to prove your worth to anyone. He and Yack would have that second chance and Lloyd would not make the same mistake again.

Bob returned from the bathroom and saw what happened. He helped Lloyd pick up the books and papers strewn about the floor. "You gotta let your right hook go. You coulda whooped that pussy! I woulda clocked the prick!"

Lloyd bowed his head. "Yeah, I know. We spent months together in isolation and I always thought of him as a friend, but I guess I was wrong."

"Dat's what it looked like ta me."

"He fucks with me again, he'll be hurtin'."

"Well, you can take 'im, fur sure."

Lloyd was upset. He should have known that tangling with Yack would not be easy. And if the perception that Yack beat him stuck, it could diminish his chances of gaining power on the ward. But he had other thoughts on his mind, like finding out who was responsible for the recent thefts.

"Did you hear about the robberies?" he asked Bob.

"Yeah, one of the kids from the back ward said somethin' about somebody stealin' stuff."

"This has been goin' on for about two weeks and the nurses don't have a clue. We gotta figure out who's doin' this shit."

Bob put his towel away and sat on the edge of his bed. "Whattaya gonna do when you find out who it is?"

"The nurses told me they want to know too, but I don't like squealin'."

Bob leaned over the side of the bed and whispered, "Well, where I come from, we handle things ourself."

Lloyd liked what he was hearing. It rang a bell inside of him. If he could figure out who it was and take care of it himself— namely kick the livin' shit out of the guy—it could go a long way to building some respect within the ward.

"I'd like to get my hands on the son-of-a-bitch!"

Bob grinned and just nodded. "Was that the guy, Lack, Mack, Dack?" He pointed to Yack.

"You mean Yack. Yeah, that's him, but I don't think he's the one who's stealin' shit."

"What's with him? He keeps calling me out, too."

"He's callin' you out?" This took Lloyd by surprise. He knew Yack had guts but this was Yack's biggest mistake.

Bob continued. "He's been sayin' shit about me... where I come from, lookin' goofy, bein' a shit-kicker and all. He doesn't even know me!"

"He's losin' it, man. He's makin' a big mistake, fuckin' with you."

"I take shit so long, then that's it. I don't take it anymore and have to do somethin' 'bout it."

Considering the size of Bob's arms, Lloyd knew he wouldn't want to be on the wrong end of those pythons. Having him as a friend was a definite plus for Lloyd. He sensed immediately that teaming up with Bob could solidify control. Tensions were running high on the ward. But with looting going on, he pledged to himself that he would figure out who was responsible.

ELEVEN

RON AND BOB'S WISDOM

Acting out of anger diminishes ability.

It was different waking up on Saturdays and Sundays. Mrs. Gipe was off, there was no school, and no therapies, and every other weekend, patients could have family visits between the hours of 2:00 to 4:00 PM. That was, of course, for those families caring enough to remain in touch.

By the summer of '66, Lloyd had only seen his family once since his admission. Correspondence was sporadic and brief. Like many who remained at the hospital indefinitely, it was natural to resent those who were ambulatory and with caring families who could go home on furlough for weekends.

Lloyd became incrementally aware that he was the person other guys wanted to be around, and whom nurses were beginning to fear. He was treated with a different type of respect. Unbeknownst to Mrs. Gipe, information that was formerly withheld from patients was given more freely to him by the staff.

Hierarchies exist on every social and biological stratum. And although an old adage states that some people rise to "their level of incompetence," hospitals are no different than any corporation, replete with nepotism and favoritism. In the hospital setting, people wield power based upon levels of education as well as socio-economic status and one's ability to coordinate or command the activities of others.

The lowest on the totem pole is invariably the custodial and groundskeeping staff, followed by lower administration. There is a blending of management and pay scale within the ranks of mid-level admin and lower-level nursing staff. Although they rank equally in administrative capabilities, upper level admin generally exceeds the pay scale of the higher nursing staff. Historically, it has been more effective to allow a clear demarcation between medical and administrative staff, with doctors holding highest esteem, although that is rarely the case. Admin is loath to relinquish too much control over the allocation of resources, even to the most highly praised, eminently skilled physicians.

Conflict arises from the traditional question, "Which comes first, the chicken or the egg?" It would be ideal to strike a balance between a well-run administration and skilled medical staff. A viable life-saving institution cannot survive without both.

In business, people rise to "their level of incompetence." Hospitals are no different.

Lloyd had been there long enough to know all the players. He held a special fondness for the housekeeping staff. For those on every level with whom he spent the most time, he found out their names, the members of their family, where they lived, how they lived and their histories. Lloyd began getting bits and pieces of information regarding upcoming events and new patients. The longer he was there, and as his rise in the ward hierarchies grew, information came from higher levels of the staff. Some nurses talked to him on the sly about his condition, progressing to details regarding his prognosis, including future surgeries. Nurses started feeding him information about other things as well. Lloyd wanted to know about the recent robberies.

One of the nurses mentioned that they, by the direction of Mrs. Gipe, had checked every cabinet for the stolen goods and found none.

Lloyd spoke to Bob about it. "I think it's gotta be someone able to walk."

Bob spoke up. "It could be someone in a wheelchair. Some of these guys move pretty fast."

"Yeah, that's true. But where would they hide the stuff?"

"Shit, I don't know this place and I can find a place to hide it. Dat's no problem."

"Yeah, but the nurses said they've been checking cabinets and shit."

"You know some of these guys. They're pretty slick."

"Let's just say the guy's able to walk."

Bob piped up. "Then, he'd be able to go home on the weekends. He'd be able to get rid of the shit on the weekends!"

"Right! And the guys in wheelchairs have been here awhile. I don't know a few of the walkers, 'cause they haven't been here that long."

"Yeah. The guys that have been here awhile wouldn't be one to rip off their buddies. Why would they rip off their own kind?"

"That's it, Bob! That narrows it down."

Bob's family didn't pick him up or visit either, so they spent a lot of time talking. They also brought in another guy on the ward Lloyd felt could not have committed the deed. Ronnie Meece got along with everyone. He was stocky, with a smaller stature and a deformed lower extremity. Ron's bed was in the back Ward 16, but with arms that would put Popeye to shame and recurring trouble healing an infection from surgery he had on his left arm, he spent most of his time riding fast in a wheelchair between the wards.

No one could beat Ron in a wheelchair race. And as much as others would complain that he had the fastest wheelchair when they lost to him, the truth was that Ron was very strong and adept with his hands. If you needed something from someone in another section of the ward, or to pass information among secret sources, Ronnie was your man. With his eyes wide open and his ears to the ground, he was a good informational source as well.

It was Ron who whispered to Lloyd, "I heard you been lookin' for the robber."

"Yeah, you hear anything in the back ward?"

"No. But I'm still lookin'."

"Do me a favor, Ron. Keep your ear to the ground and let me know."

"I will. Hey, by the way, if you need a little squeeze, Glenda's been talkin' 'boutya."

"Really? What'd she say?"

Ronnie looked around, as though someone might be listening. "She mentioned it while she was doin' my bed this morning."

This intrigued Lloyd. "Have you tried it with her?"

"Oh, yeah. This morning, when she was making my bed, I tried it with her and she let me touch her. And when I said we should go a little farther, she said no. So, I said that she must be gettin' a lot at home. She said no again. But then she said that she wouldn't kick Lloyd out of her bed."

"She said my name?"

"Yeah. She said, 'I wouldn't kick Lloyd out of my bed, if he wanted me'."

"Thanks, Ron. I could use a little action right now."

Lloyd's imagination reverted to his experience with Maggie in isolation. Glenda was a nurse's aide, married with four children. At 5'11", she was 35 years young and all muscle. With a sandy-colored pageboy haircut, bright green eyes, and a turned up nose, she had average sized breasts with wide hips, strong arms and thighs like tree trunks. Glenda was no-nonsense, strictly business. She got through each day as quickly and with as little fanfare as she could. She was the muscle Mrs. Gipe called to do the heavy lifting. Glenda could come in, flip you over, and be on her way before you had time to react. Lloyd vowed to have his way with her.

As often as he thought of Glenda, and what he could do with her, Lloyd was also thinking that it was just a matter of time before whoever was ripping people off would try to take his stuff as well. And Lloyd was amassing quite a collection. There was a lot of baseball card trading.

Glenda could come in, flip you over, and be on her way before you had time to react. Lloyd vowed to have his way with her.

His immediate objective one Saturday morning in July was to find a place where he, Bob, and Ron could talk about the robberies and not be overheard. The playroom with the stereo was the perfect place.

The day was bright and sunny, the air fresh and crisp from the morning dew. After getting help being put on a stretcher, he began the slow sojourn to the playroom, pushing off the bedposts, straight to the door, then working diagonally from wall to wall out into the hallway. Inside the playroom, Lloyd positioned himself in front of the glass doors of the boy's ward porch, adjacent to the stereo, where he could soak up optimal sunlight.

There was a small group of kids from the back ward already there playing a card game. When Bob and Ron joined him, Lloyd immediately dismissed the group. "Hey guys, go back to the ward. We got somethin' we need to talk about."

They paused with puzzled looks. They were younger, didn't know Lloyd that well, and showed minimal response. They then stared at Ronnie who just gave a silent nod and motioned for them to leave. Without a word, all three wheeled out.

Lloyd was impressed, realizing that he had a power player with him in Ron Meese. He hadn't forgotten about Marvin Sparks from the back ward, and wondered whether Ron was making a power grab, too.

He started the discussion. "We gotta find out who's ripping people off! Ron, whattaya know about the guys from the back ward?"

"There's a coupla assholes back there, but nobody I could put my finger on. We have a way with takin' care of people that fuck around like this."

Bob nodded in agreement and slammed his right fist into his left palm.

Lloyd wanted revenge too, but had a much deeper anger he had to share. "Yeah, we'll take care of 'em when we catch 'em. But it pisses me off that one of us is rippin' us off!"

Bob floated an idea he had been kicking around. "It's queer that the nurses don't say anything about it... like maybe they got somethin' to gain by all this."

That made Lloyd wonder. "Now, we know it's not the guys in body-casts or hip-spicas. They couldn't move fast enough to get away. It's gotta be someone in a wheelchair or walking, that moves fast enough so people wouldn't see 'em. And I think it's someone who goes home on furlough, 'cause the nurses haven't found the shit in anybody's cabinet. So, whoever's doin' this must be takin' the shit home with 'em and gettin' rid of it on the weekends."

"That brings the number way down," Ron chimed in. "Don't look at me! I never go home!"

"You're all right, Ron. Who's left in the back?"

He shook it off. "That's easy."

"Ron, I need names!"

"That leaves Jimmy Openfus, Kenny Mauer, and Raymond Augers."

Lloyd added to the list. "We have Joel Hooker, Billy Williams, Jackie Withers, and Bob Throcton in the front ward. I know Joel and Bill wouldn't do it, but I'm not sure of Jack Withers or Bob Throcton."

Bob was anxious. "Let's start with them then." With that he slammed his right fist hard into his left palm again.

This made Ron jump.

Lloyd said, "We'll talk to them first. When Jackie Withers comes back from furlough, tell him I want to talk to him. We'll start with that."

When he finished, a vision appeared in the doorway. It was Glenda.

Twelve

THE CULPRIT AND THE PLEDGE

"[He] who overcomes by force
hath overcome but half his foe."
–John Milton

Glenda stood in the doorway, tall and resolute. With hands on her hips, she announced, "Lloyd, we need the stretcher and I've been told to put you back to bed."

He didn't argue with Glenda. He was too attracted to her. Turning to Bob and Ron, he said, "We'll talk later, guys." Then Lloyd acquiesced to Glenda. "Okay. Would you mind pushing me back?"

Just watching her walk toward him washed clean any other thought pattern.

"That's why I'm here." Her voice was soft and conciliatory.

Lloyd began to wonder whether what Ron told him about her was true, or if Ron was just setting him up to get slapped by the feminine fantasy he created.

Lloyd wondered whether she would push him from his feet or his head. If she took the stretcher by his feet, he wouldn't have the opportunity to put his hands on her.

She said, "Hold on, here we go," and proceeded to take control of the stretcher at the top.

She maneuvered the vehicle smoothly to the door, leaning forward as she pushed. Lloyd held on to the top part of the transport. When they were clear of the playroom, outside the ward and beyond eyesight, she stood more erect and closer to the top of the stretcher. As they neared the ward, Glenda put her hips against Lloyd's hands to propel the stretcher to his bed. He could feel her hips rubbing against him as she walked. He took this as a partial affirmation and placed both hands on the upper portion of each of her ample thighs and began rubbing vigorously. She slowed the stretcher as he migrated closer to her womanhood.

She paused momentarily, against the far wall in a darkened area just outside of the ward. Lloyd kept up his deep massage, working his way down. It wasn't long before Glenda noticed the approach of one of the nurses. She stood more erect and well beyond Lloyd's reach. Carefully, and with one fluid motion, she resumed her push to the ward.

When they arrived at his bedside, she stood back, then casually pulled his curtain closed and moved to the bottom of the stretcher. She placed his legs in the center of the bed as he moved his torso to transfer from the stretcher. She then pulled the stretcher back and began fluffing the pillows surrounding his head, a practice normally left to the patient.

Lloyd was on his stomach and had easy access to caress her legs with his right hand. He had to find out if she was receptive to that idea.

Repeating the maneuver he'd perfected with Maggie in isolation, he dropped his right arm off the side of the bed. As he did, she moved forcefully against his arm. With that, he gradually moved his hand to the back on her left thigh. He was pleasantly surprised that he felt her flesh—she wore no stockings! He was also surprised by the width and sinew of the muscles of her legs.

He cautiously moved his hand up under her uniform and as he did, she moved closer to the bed and leaned over him to straighten the sheets on the opposite side, pressing her breasts on the back of his head. He relished the feel of her stiff bra, took this to be his "green light," and reached for her buttocks.

She wore thin cotton panties. As he massaged her buttocks, Glenda bent down, wrapped her arms around him and lovingly kissed him on the back of his neck. His mind began to explode.

As he reached within her panties and the magical confine between her thighs, his euphoria ended abruptly.

"Glenda, where's that stretcher?"

Glenda bent down, wrapped her arms around him and lovingly kissed him on the back of his neck.

As though struck by lightning, Glenda jumped up and pulled the curtain back. She quickly grabbed the stretcher and was on her way. But as she was leaving, she whispered to him, "You have strong hands. Thanks for the massage."

He only saw her in passing after that, but it was a great fantasy while it lasted.

Many of those remaining at the hospital over the weekend were already in the playroom Sunday night. They sneered as the furloughed people waddled past.

"There they are!"

"Hey, strangers!"

Lloyd saw Jack Withers walk by with his duffle bag. He was impressed when, within ten minutes, Ronnie followed Withers in. Bob and Lloyd were waiting for him. They had a small area cordoned off by the stereo.

Jack was understandably puzzled. "You wanted to talk to me, Lloyd?"

"Yeah. Sit down, Jack."

Bob pushed him a chair right next to Lloyd's stretcher. Bob then pulled his chair around and with Ronnie's wheelchair, essentially locked him in their circle. Tall and lanky at 5'9", towering over the three interrogators, Jack wasn't afraid. Recovering from surgery to his right foot and ankle, a congenital deformity, he had a cast that extended from his right knee covering his right foot. With pins in each toe, the cast had a walking rubber knob on the bottom that allowed him mobility. His condition was considered mild in comparison to most. He was a fast-tracker.

"So, what's goin' on, guys?" Jack wondered.

Lloyd reached out and put his hand on Jack's shoulder. "Just relax. I want to find out what your schedule is like."

"This is about the robberies, isn't it?"

"Yes, it is."

"Well, *I* didn't do anything!" With that, he stood up.

Bob also stood and shoved his chest into Jack's, making the latter fall back against Lloyd's stretcher.

"Hey, I'm not gonna be pushed around!"

Lloyd grabbed Jack's belt and turned him. With a calm voice, he stared up at him, directly into his eyes. "Sit down, Jack." Pulling him closer still, he repeated, "Sit down, and keep your voice down!"

Jack was shaking, but continued standing.

Lloyd repeated the command, this time more calmly. "Sit down, Jack."

Unruffling his shirt, Jack turned to look at Bob who was standing ready to pounce, and slowly took his seat again. The other kids in the playroom knew something was up and cautiously shuffled out.

Lloyd watched the leaving parade and knew he didn't have too much more time before someone would mention something to one of the nurses.

"Okay, Jack. I want to know what your schedule was the day before yesterday. And if you can't tell me, I'll find out what it was and if it doesn't add up, we'll be talkin' again!"

Bob bellowed, "And next time, we won't be talkin'!"

Jack started to rub his hands vigorously. Lloyd put his hand on Jack's shoulder. "Jack, just tell us what your schedule was like on Friday."

Now, Jack was afraid. He looked at Lloyd and Bob and then, Ron. Ron spoke up. "Go ahead, Jack. Tell 'em."

Jack leaned back and took a deep breath. "Well, after I got up and had breakfast, got cleaned up, I went to school, back to the ward at noon and then, back to school. From school, I went to PT."

Lloyd asked, "What do you do when you're in PT?"

The physical therapy department was a large room down the hall, set off in a wing to the right of the lobby. For most patients, their time in therapy was part of their socialization. The boys could hang out, meet girls, try to make time with some of the therapists or their assistants, and fake their exercise just to keep from going back to the ward.

Jack proceeded to give them a detailed account of the leg-lifts, bicycle, walking stairs, bicep development with five-pound dumbbells, and so on. He was back in the ward by 5:00 PM.

They knew the deed had already been done by then.

This process continued for interviewing two guys from the front ward and one other guy from the back ward before they got to a guy named Raymond Augers.

Raymond let Ron know without equivocating, "I will not meet with you or anybody else! I don't have to!" He also told Ron and the others that, "If any of you try any muscle on me, I'll go right to the nurses, or Miss Laux!"

This was quite a threat. Word had already circulated that these meetings were not a congeniality contest. Although, at the time, the nurses were beginning to lose control of the ward, they were one level Raymond could appeal to for protection. Miss Laux was a whole other formidable level.

Standing all of 5'6", Miss Laux wielded her power as coolly as hardened steel and held dominion over all living objects within the hospital. Even under extreme conditions, her manner remained calm and reassured. Miss Laux did not suffer stupidity or insubordination. Her name was pronounced, "locks," as a subtle reminder of her ability to clamp down dissent of any kind.

Miss Laux was aware of Lloyd's rise in stature on the ward, and on a number of occasions, made it known to him that she did not approve of his attitude. She came out of her office, located in the center of the main lobby, and impeded Lloyd's progress down the hall to physical therapy. "I understand, Mr. Negoescu, that you questioned whether you should have taken your medication last night."

Lloyd was always on-guard where she was concerned. "No, Miss Laux. I only questioned that they were the correct medications, not that I should or should not take them. I believe that is my right."

Miss Laux—her name was pronounced "locks" as a subtle reminder of her ability to clamp down dissent of any kind.

"I take it, Mr. Negoescu, that you question whether the drugs you are receiving are correct. Is that true?"

"Miss Laux, I always check what I put in my mouth."

"You should be more concerned with what comes out of your mouth, Mr. Negoescu." With that, she gracefully moved to one side, looked at the orderly and waved them on.

Always cool and aloof, the woman was without emotion. A thorn in Lloyd's side, she was the classic antagonist to his protagonist. Where Lloyd remained a staunch defender of patient rights, she was the bulwark that resisted challenge on any level. There weren't many details, even on a minute scale, she overlooked. She intimidated even the doctors.

If any patient challenged her, she would quietly threaten to cut off all privileges. If that wasn't enough, the patient could spend more time in bed, with no mobility on a stretcher. If all else failed, she would have the doctors prescribe large doses of Valium to subdue them.

Lloyd slowly and methodically made it clear to her that he had little or nothing to lose by resisting her, a lesson he almost fatally lost much later in his stay.

She had ordered another change of bed position, attempting to split him up from Bob. The move was a direct result of an encounter she and Lloyd had over his cut-off, sleeveless t-shirt. As Lloyd's arms started to develop, he felt good about exposing them more, and with the heat of the summer of 1966, he pulled his sleeves above his shoulders. Yack, always the innovator, came up with the idea of cutting off the sleeves so the edges were ragged and threadbare. The desired look was more casual and a bit on the rough side.

As an orderly was pushing Lloyd's stretcher to class one day, they navigated past Miss Laux's office. Ever the eagle eye, she caught Lloyd flying by and leapt from her chair. "Hold it, right there!"

The orderly stopped on a dime. Lloyd cringed. It was mid-morning and the lobby was bustling with administrative staff and patients.

He was stuck out in the middle of the lobby. Miss Laux emerged from her office and advanced toward Lloyd's stretcher, arms folded. Sauntering around him, she approached from behind. Without a word, she stood over him and as she fingered his frayed shirtsleeves, all activity around them stopped.

The rotunda of the lobby was huge, at least fifty feet in diameter, with a thirty-foot ceiling, well-polished floor and little furniture. Numerous offices of all shapes and sizes surrounded it, from which exited and entered a constant stream of people conducting business. It was the focal point of the building, and the din of footsteps, beds, stretchers and wheelchairs echoed throughout the day. It shocked Lloyd that the clamor suddenly turned into the silence of a library, in which only the sound of Miss Laux's voice could be heard.

"In the future, Mr. Negoescu, you will wear regular t-shirts. There will be no more cutting off sleeves."

Her calm delivery did little to diminish her voice in the bare-walled chamber. Lloyd lay there staring straight ahead, trying to ignore her.

"Did you hear what I said, Mr. Negoescu?"

Lloyd looked around and could see she was drawing an audience. He thought, *Good!* "I make it a habit not to listen to what you have to say, Miss Laux!"

Without flinching, stoically, she just stood there with her arms still folded, glaring. "Very well then, Mr. Negoescu. I suppose you will hear me when I tell you that you are grounded for a week."

Lloyd stared straight ahead in defiance.

As though choreographed for the benefit of the onlookers, she turned to the orderly and waved him off. "Take him away!"

The orderly, George, bowed his head and pushed the stretcher forward. As he did, the commotion in the lobby slowly picked up as people went about their business. Miss Laux stood glaring at Lloyd for only a few seconds before casually re-entering her office.

George was impressed. As they moved further away from her, he whispered, "That's tellin' 'er. You got balls, kid. I'll give ye that!"

Lloyd smiled, hiding his fear. He knew that unless you were oblivious or a total idiot, you didn't cross Miss Laux without worrying about some form of retribution.

Opposing forces, she and Lloyd had few things they could agree on. Where Lloyd's interest was in acquiring more freedom, her primary interest was retaining the status quo. So, when Raymond made it known that he would go to Miss Laux if he had to, Lloyd knew he and Raymond would have to have a reckoning.

Lloyd told Bob, "The first chance you get, when Raymond comes through the front ward to get to the back, stop him and bring him over."

Bob was only too happy to oblige. He had been prodding Lloyd to let him pop somebody. Lloyd held him back. That night, Lloyd was already in bed when Raymond came trotting through the front ward.

Now, although he was a member of the back ward, Raymond was not a small kid. At about 5'4", he was wiry but strong. He bragged, "I come from South Philly, and I don't take shit from nobody!"

He was a fast-tracker, already had his surgery, and was about to head home in the next week or so. That night, as soon as Raymond reached the edge of Ward 14, Bob jumped out, grabbed him and shoved him hard in Lloyd's direction.

Lloyd took hold of him and threw him into a chair, wrapping Raymond's arms back behind the chair, locking him in place.

Raymond screamed, "Heyyyyyyy!"

Lloyd nodded to Ron who was at the other end of the ward, watching for the nurses. Ron looked back and gave Lloyd the okay sign.

Bob rushed over with a pillow and put it over Raymond's face, pushing his head back against Lloyd's chest.

Lloyd whispered, "Ray, you come clean and we let you go."

Raymond shook against him, but Lloyd held firm. Lloyd gave Bob the look he was waiting for. When Lloyd pulled the pillow away, all Ray saw was a hard right cross catch him smack on the left side of the face. Ray's head snapped back and hit Lloyd hard in the chest. Spittle from Ray's mouth splattered Lloyd's forehead. He then went limp. Lloyd thought he was out. Bob just smiled.

Raymond came around and shook his head. With tears in his eyes, he started crying, "I only took money! I'll pay it back!"

Lloyd was pissed and shook him. He was also shocked this asshole gave up so easily. He spoke in little above a whisper, "You took a lot more than that, you fuckin' bastard!"

It was at that moment that Lloyd noticed the entire ward was quiet; everyone was looking over at them. Stuart Margolies lifted himself up in his body cast and started to scream, "I want my St. Christopher's medal back! I want my St. Christopher's medal back!"

Raymond yelled, "I got rid of it at home. It wasn't worth anything!"

Lloyd hadn't noticed that Lurch, the little kid with Muscular Dystrophy, already in the death throes of his disease, was making his way slowly toward them in his wheelchair, his movements barely a crawl. When Lurch reached Lloyd's bed, Bob was ready to hit Raymond again. Lloyd had a death grip on Ray's arms. Raymond wasn't going anywhere.

Lurch reached them. Lloyd thought he just wanted to get a better view, but all of sudden, Lurch lunged forward and with his frail, splintered little arms, he balled up his tiny fist and planted a fantastic punch on the same side of Ray's face that Bob had just plastered.

POW!

Lloyd was impressed! "Very good, Lurch!"

Lurch spat at Raymond. "That's for takin' my hard-earned money!"

Raymond snarled, "I'll get you later, you little prick!"

Lloyd drew Raymond's arms back harder and almost snapped his shoulders free of his torso. "You so much as touch him, and I'll break both your arms!"

Just as Lloyd finished the warning, Bob planted another good shot on the left side of Ray's face, this time sending him reeling so wild, he fell off the chair onto the floor.

Bob leaned into him and wanted to send him another when Lloyd reached out with his right arm. "That's enough!"

Raymond lay on the floor between the two beds. Lloyd thought it a fitting place, since the nurses wouldn't see. Raymond stayed down and held his face, crying. He was all right.

Lurch tried to run Raymond over with his wheelchair and Lloyd had to hold him back as well. "It's okay, Lurch. He's had enough."

Lurch tried to run Raymond over with his wheelchair.

Lloyd loved Lurch. Here was someone who was the most severely physically challenged of all of them, and yet his perception remained clear and always appropriate. He always spoke the truth and, when challenged by some of the biggest kids, he never backed down. Although Lloyd looked out for him, he never had to take him under his wing. Lurch was fiercely independent.

As for Raymond Augers, most of the back ward and a few guys in the front ward beat him senseless, all trying to recover what he stole from them, extracting their pound of flesh.

When he ran to Miss Laux and she made her perfunctory appearance before each ward, so many had taken part in kicking Raymond's ass that no one spoke up. She glared at Lloyd the whole time. When she passed his bed on the way out, she leaned down and spoke to him alone. "I know you're responsible for this."

Lloyd just smiled.

None of the kids were able to recover the stolen property. Raymond had squandered it all and was discharged shortly thereafter.

But Bob Walters' insight came back to Lloyd. *It's queer that the nurses don't say anything about it... like maybe they got somethin' to gain by all this.*

The administration sat on their hands while kids were being ripped off by that asshole. Usually, the more the patients turned to the nurses and administration for emotional support, the more acquiescent and compliant they could become. For good or bad, that didn't happen. The patients became their own best support.

It became a veritable *Lord of the Flies*.

The next day Bob came to Lloyd after school. "We need to talk."

His serious demeanor surprised Lloyd. "Okay. When?"

"Later."

As Bob walked away, Lloyd was left wondering, *What the hell?*

After dinner that night Bob strolled up to Lloyd's bed and produced a switchblade from under his shirt.

Lloyd waved his arms. "Whoa, what's that for?"

Bob pulled up a chair and characteristically turned it to straddle the seat. As he leaned forward, smiling, he looked around to see if the coast was clear. In one smooth motion, he flicked the knife, splaying the long blade in front of Lloyd.

Bob's non-threatening demeanor did not put Lloyd at ease. Leaning on his right elbow, Lloyd had to define the moment. "Alllllll-right. What are we doing?"

Bob flicked the knife, splaying the long blade in front of Lloyd.

Despite his attempts to avoid attention, when Bob flicked his knife, a crowd appeared out of the woodwork, probably assuming he was about to carve up Lloyd!

Bob leaned closer to Lloyd and spoke softly with great sobriety. "You don't know this, but I'm part American Indian. My grandparents were members of the Sioux tribe. In my tribe you bind your closest friendships by becoming blood brothers. I think we should do that."

Lloyd didn't know what that really meant, other than that with Bob wielding such a sharp blade, it would mean some measure of pain. Still, he was honored.

Bob raised both hands in front of him. "Being blood brothers means that at any time in my life, if I get into trouble, I can call you and you'll come to help me. And if you get into trouble, you can call me and I'll come to help you."

Lloyd was dumbfounded. He never had an equal who felt so committed to him. He wondered whether he was worthy of such admiration. He looked around at the other guys who were also present. They were all keeping a safe distance, but remained alert.

Then he turned back to Bob. "It would mean a lot to me to be your blood brother. What do we do?"

"Well, my knife is sharp so you have to be very still when I cut your hand."

"Okay, then what?"

"You cut my hand and we hold our hands in an Indian handshake, like this." He took Lloyd's right hand with his and they locked thumbs tightly, then he closed his fist with both hands clenched with arms touching to the elbow.

Lloyd smiled. "Okay, let's do it!"

"Give me your right hand."

Bob took Lloyd's right hand and turned it upright. Carefully, holding the knife between his thumb and index finger, Bob slowly and methodically sliced a long thin line from just below Lloyd's fingerprint area to the bottom knuckle of his right thumb. The cut wasn't deep. There was not much blood, and because the knife was sharp, there was very little pain.

Lloyd's fear began when Bob handed him the knife and thrust his upturned right hand for him to cut. Lloyd wasn't as adept. He cut deeper, and there was far more blood, but Bob didn't so much as wince.

Dripping blood, Bob stood, reached out, grasped Lloyd's right hand with only the strength Bob could muster, and they locked tightly. As they held this embrace for an extended time, Bob wrapped his left hand around their locked hands. Lloyd took his cue and topped Bob's.

They shook, palms mashed together to ensure full blood exchange, and Bob began to recite the pledge, "I, Bob Walters, vow to always come to the aid of my brother, Lloyd Negoescu, no matter what he needs or where he is, or what I'm doing."

Lloyd then, made the same pledge to Bob. "I, Lloyd Negoescu, vow to always come to the aid of my brother, Bob Walters, no matter what he needs or where he is, or what I'm doing."

Whether they would ever have fulfilled their commitment to each other, Lloyd found it difficult to imagine a more solemn moment in his life.

THIRTEEN

AFTER-HOURS VISITOR

There are as many varied degrees of freedom
as there is the ability of the mind to dream.

Any stint at E-town Children's Hospital was a rite of passage. Beyond normal pangs and frustrations, here was a place that accepted those exiled from all they held sacred. However crudely they administered, the staff made it their commitment to at least minimally restore broken depressed souls a modicum of normality.

Lloyd was unhappy that Miss Laux split him and Bob apart, but he loved his new bed position. Pushed against the opposite corner of the ward, he was further from the nurse's station than ever. His bed was adjacent to two glass-paneled doors to his left, giving him access to a small screened-in balcony out front. With the increased heat of late summer, it was a great relief at night. To top that, his cubicle mate was someone young and oblivious to current politics. Lloyd couldn't have asked for more. But he did.

After "lights out," a woman in her early thirties walked through the ward and hand delivered something to Yack. Her perfume was intoxicating and hung in the air like a calling card. Lloyd said hello, as many of the guys did. All were feeble attempts to get her attention. She just smiled blissfully and continued on.

Lloyd found out from Yack that her name was Helen and she delivered mail from the girl's ward to some of the guys. With the high level of tension that existed between patients and staff, the best part about her repeated appearances was that Helen didn't draw the attention of the nurses. She glided through and was gone before anyone at the nursing station was the wiser.

Helen was cute. At 5'2", she was thin, but shapely. "The perfect Coke-bottle," as many of the boys would attest. She had shoulder-length, rich black hair and full lips surrounding a great smile. Her one-piece uniform traveled well below her knees, but high enough to expose her starched white bobby socks and impeccably clean saddle shoes.

Helen was cute... thin, but shapely. "The perfect Coke-bottle."

Born and raised in Pennsylvania Dutch country, Helen's family was Mennonite, and practiced a more relaxed dress code. Although Helen attended public school, her parents restricted her dating anyone until she reached the age of maturity. She started working at E-town after graduation, remaining aloof to the clumsy advances of members of the opposite sex, while keenly aware of the rules regarding fraternization, especially with teenage suitors.

Lloyd knew that if he were to make his intentions for her clear, his approach would have to be unique. With the experience of Maggie while in isolation still fresh, and although twice his age, Helen was another quest he simply could not resist. Besides, challenge be damned, this was a woman!

One evening as she strolled through the ward, he called to her. "Excuse me. Could you help me with something?"

His use of the politeness may have intrigued her. She slowed at the base of his bed. "What could I *possibly* do for you?"

Her tone put him on guard. This would be no easy catch. He scrambled for what to say next. "Could you spend some time with me? I need someone to talk to."

She sighed, obviously disappointed by the standard line. "I wish I could stay, but I really have to be going." With that, she abruptly turned and walked on.

Lloyd heard a few murmured snickers to confirm that they were not the only ones to fail with this beauty. As he drank in the remnants of her aroma and licked his ego-wounds, he resolved that he would try another approach next time.

Life continued as usual, with Mrs. Gipe banging her metal drum in the morning, school classes before and after lunch, ending the day with therapy in the late afternoon. Despite the confines of a highly conservative environment and an over-zealous matriarchal nursing director, there were quiet, less conspicuous folks who understood the value of freedom of expression.

George, the maintenance man was one. Another was a diminutive individual, Mrs. Wittle, an apt name for one whose chosen profession was cutting hair. Mrs. Wittle was a short, stout, matronly woman who glided through all wards of the hospital leaving neatly trimmed skulls in her wake. Lloyd had numerous conversations with her and was always amazed how courteous she remained. Whenever she was called upon to do so, she entered the room, introduced herself and went straight to work.

"I notice you cut everyone's hair. Who would you say has the hardest hair to cut?"

"Everyone's hair is different. You can't predict how a haircut should go. You have to follow the flow of the hair on the head."

"But it must be hard to cut someone's hair that's in a cast, right?"

"Oh, sure! But I find that if you're kind and have them positioned in such a way, I can pretty much get to where I have to go to cut all their hair."

Although not entirely happy, Lloyd was pleased she refrained from chopping off too much. He recognized that her job was not easy in the turbulent '60s with boys who wanted their hair as long as possible. Mrs. Wittle did her utmost to conform to the wishes of the administration and nursing staff, while being sympathetic to the desires of teenage boys striving to uphold the tenets of a radical youth culture.

Throughout this period though, Helen remained uppermost in Lloyd's mind. He didn't see her for at least three nights and had plenty of time to prepare for his next encounter. As she reached his bed on her way out this time, he was more direct. "Excuse me, I have a question."

"Yes."

"Is your name Helen?"

"Yes."

"My name's Lloyd."

"I know. I've heard about you." She said it in not so pleasing a manner.

"Oh, so you heard about me, huh?"

"Yeah, I've heard about *you*." She emphasized the last word.

"Well, I hope it was good."

"Not really!"

"Oh." That threw him for a moment, but he knew he had to get back on track or lose her again. "I notice that you deliver messages from the girl's ward."

"Yes, but that's not for public notice. I could get in trouble."

"What if I wrote *you* a note?"

"Don't do that. If somebody found it, I could lose my job."

She was starting to turn to leave when he hit her with one more question. "If I can't write you a letter and you won't stay long enough to hear me out, how can I tell you what I want you to know?"

Perhaps it was his voice, his manner of speech, his less-threatening tone, or that it was late and she was just tired. Whatever it was, it compelled her to move closer.

Hovering at the base of his bed, keeping a safe distance, she spoke in hushed tones so as not to be detected by the nurses. "Okay, what is it you want me to know?"

He wasn't sure he had her, and didn't want to blow it. His answer was a sigh of relief. "I want you to know how I feel about you."

She laughed, almost lasciviously. "Uh-huh, I'll bet you do!"

He had to think fast now. "Now, you see? You already made up your mind about what I feel."

Obviously, she didn't have too many patients challenge her intellectually, but in her unique style, she handled it with ease. "I think I know what feelings you have for me... or any woman in here."

"You think you know, but you really don't know for sure, right?"

She was determined. "I think what I think."

He answered quickly. "But you don't know."

She sighed in frustration and turned to leave. "I have to go."

He didn't want her to leave, but had no choice in the matter. "Could we talk tomorrow? I have more I want you to know."

"I don't work tomorrow. Thursday, maybe."

He was relieved; at least he got another date. "Okay, Thursday then." With that, she left him.

Trying to think of what had just happened, he wondered whether this banter would be worth it, or that perhaps he had challenged her too much. *Why do these women have to make it so tough? Why not just crawl in bed with me?* She was older than him by quite a few years, and he wasn't sure he could keep up with her intellectually. All he could envision was the struggle he'd had with Maggie and how long that process took.

> *Why do these women have to make it so tough? Why not just crawl in bed with me?*

Thursday came and went. He didn't see Helen for another two weeks and wondered whether he had said something that put her off. When she did finally come strolling through the ward, she stopped at his bed before leaving, to ask him a question. "Have you been thinking about our conversation since our last talk?"

Now Lloyd was even more dumbfounded. He didn't have a clue, but knew he'd better come up with something quick. "I was wondering what you think I think about women."

That stopped her cold. "What I think you think about women... hmm."

"Yeah..." And here he trailed off, still thinking how to explain his position. "Because if you think that I think nothin' but bad thoughts about women, then you must think I'm just some kinda pervert or somethin'."

She stepped closer and whispered deliberately, but with a smirk. "I don't think you are a pervert or I wouldn't give you the time of day!"

This was his opening. "Can we talk?"

She answered quickly. "Aren't we talking now?"

"Are we? Are we really talking, or just sparring over simple details?" He didn't want to alienate her, but had to give it a shot.

She didn't give in that easy. "You'll have to define 'sparring' for me."

From there, the conversation continued for another ten minutes of semantic banter. She was always in control, and he only flailed to stay afloat and keep up.

Lloyd's interest was always clear— he wanted her and would do anything to get her.

This routine was repeated, on and off, for the next two months. She didn't show up that often, so Lloyd's chances to impress her were sporadic. His interest was always clear—he wanted her and would do anything to get her. But at the same time, he couldn't help thinking that she was playing mind games with him, toying with his emotions. After all, the relationship hadn't progressed beyond verbal wrangling. With her arms folded at all times, and her standing at the base of his bed, she wouldn't get near enough to him to allow any physical contact.

Helen's behavior was not that unusual. Sexual repression, in that part of Pennsylvania, was part of the culture. His pleasure was her allowing him to bask in her beauty a few moments each week. He also hoped that the combination of her patience and his tenacity to win her over would prove fruitful at a later date.

FOURTEEN

BASEBALL, SEX, AND A CLOSE CALL

*All too often, methods of conveying love and
affection fall on deaf ears and blind eyes.*

It should be noted that Lloyd's predisposition, since the age of
sexual awareness, had been, if not obsessed, as close to an
obsession about the opposite sex as anyone could possibly get.
Lloyd realized that many of his colleagues would brag about
their obsessions, and that as those closest to him would attest,
there had never been a more paramount thought in his mind
than that of the female psyche, and foremost even more
prominently, the feminine physique.

At any given time of day, conversations involving the
opposite sex were commonplace. Those younger would always
gravitate to older groups to pick up whatever knowledge they
could glean.

There is code for any language and any subject. On the older
boy's ward, sex had a code of its own.

If someone were asked the common question while dating
someone, "How far did you get?" that meant that one of your
cohorts was inquiring as to the freedoms allowed by your
partner during a sexual encounter. It was also common
parlance to answer in baseball terms like "first base," "second
base," "third base," and "home run."

It was rare when a description concluded with, "Yeah, I got
to first base!" Usually, getting to first base was the minimum
you could expect. When you had to admit it, the use of the term

was more a declarative statement when accused of *not* getting anywhere with someone.

"I'll bet you didn't touch her at all!"

"That's not true. I at least got to first base!"

Guys exaggerate. With wide latitude for interpretation given the baseball analogy, first base, most often, was the best a person could hope for. That usually implied that partners touched each other superficially, while kissing with clothes on.

Second base meant that they were not only able to kiss a girl on the lips, but feel her breasts and possibly touch the fringes of her vagina. Here the individual entered into a groping stage of the game, which implied even greater access to otherwise forbidden parts of the female anatomy. While this was a major objective, most teenage boys were unaware that without relief they could inevitably suffer the dreaded condition "blue balls" afterward.

Wikipedia defines "blue balls" as:

> *"...a slang term for the condition of temporary fluid congestion (vasocongestion) in the testicles and prostate region, accompanied by acute testicular pain, or a prolonged dull aching pain emanating from the prostate, caused by prolonged and unsatisfied sexual arousal in the human male."*

Third base was always rewarding, because while toying with each other in the first two stages of lovemaking, there was no relief, no discharge or ejaculation. Third base, if nothing else, provided the necessary release for both partners short of complete penetration. People could stroke, rub, and perform fellatio or cunnilingus on each other, working into complete frenzy and ejaculate, as long as there was no penal anal/vaginal penetration.

"Home" or the "home-run" was always the ultimate objective of anyone remotely attracted to their partner. This stage included all of the preceding stages with penetration in any of its forms and positions. Although, taken a bit too cavalierly today, this was by far the premier sexual aspiration in 1966 and highly revered. The group would hold anyone reaching such stature in the highest esteem.

The corner bed position awarded Lloyd other freedoms as well. With access to a small balcony and fresh air, Lloyd purchased cigarettes off of George, the orderly, and started lighting up after lights out. He had no desire to smoke and never inhaled, but it was all part of the package. In full view, he knew the guys would be impressed.

The corner bed position awarded Lloyd other freedoms.

He had to be careful though. It had to be done at night and when the supervisor on duty was older and moved slower. The supervising nurse's schedule ran like clockwork. Their routine was to walk through each ward on opposite ends of the building, meet with their respective ward staff on the first floor, take the elevator on each end to the upstairs, then backtrack to the director's office. It wasn't hard to predict when and where they would be at a set time. The most opportune time for Lloyd was to wait until she passed through his ward the first time on her appointed rounds. Without interference from the other ward nurses, that should give him ample time to light up and display his smoking prowess. But his arrogance almost got the better of him.

The rush of cool air relieved the stagnant swelter as Lloyd opened the small balcony glass doors beside his bed. Long after lights out, there was stirring among some of the older boys, but for the most part, the ward was settled. The squeak of the latch on the door didn't disturb his much younger cubicle-mate who was already asleep. The night supervisor had already made her initial pass through the ward, so he was assured that with her meeting the nurses of Wards 14 and 16 and the upstairs Wards 24 and 26, he had plenty of time.

Lloyd carefully opened his nightstand to reach the well-concealed pack of cigarettes taped to the back wall of the drawer. The drawer was not well oiled and creaked with each pull, but once he dislodged the parcel, the loudest sound was his unraveling the crinkle plastic wrap.

He ripped open the aluminum-coated paper cover at the top, pulled out a cigarette and touched it to his lips. The smell of the fresh tobacco and the taste of the delicate paper at the tip excited him. Lying there with the long white extension dangling from his mouth, he was transported to another plane. He even made it a point to pause and peruse the room to be sure everyone got a chance to see what was happening. His objective was clear, light the cigarette, take as many puffs as he could before any nurse approached, then flick it out the open doorway.

But he had to be careful. He didn't want to move too hastily. Dropping anything, including the cigarette, the matches, or the pack, could be disastrous. If they hit any part of the bed in the fall, they could bounce

But he had to be careful...

or roll beyond his reach. He couldn't afford the luxury of a misstep. He had a public watching and a reputation he was establishing.

Lloyd held the cigarette between his lips and looked out the open doorway. Casually he opened the matchbook, bent a stick, separated it from its cradle, struck it hard against the sandpaper, and cupped his hands for the first pull. The harsh burn of the smoke scratched deeply the inside of his mouth. It took all he had to keep himself from gagging uncontrollably. He had to remain calm and self-assured, even though he could feel the tissue on the back of his throat begin to boil.

She wasn't completely out of sync, but when the night supervisor appeared at the opposite end of the ward, it threw him off. *She was supposed to go to the elevator and check in upstairs before returning*, Lloyd thought. For some reason she cut her circuit short.

The supervisor shifted toward the open doorway. As she entered the opposite end of his ward, in the dim light, Lloyd could see she was fixed on his position. With each flop of her heavy feet, he knew he had to act fast. He quickly flicked the cigarette out the door with one hand and pulled his dresser drawer open with the other. She must have been aware that there was something strange with his midnight behavior because her direction never wavered. She headed straight for him.

Once she was within a few feet, she could easily detect the strong smell of tobacco both in the air and on his breath. Lloyd hadn't prepared with deodorant spray, toothpaste, or gum. Halfway across the ward, she was in clear sight of him when he casually reached in and pulled out his Ice Blue Secret deodorant paste. As she narrowed the distance, out of desperation he unscrewed the lid, licked a huge gob, threw it back in and quietly closed the drawer.

"What are you up to, Lloyd?"

Swishing the disgusting swill around his mouth, he mumbled, "Nothing."

Wary, she stared at him for a moment, then neared his bed. The deodorant hit the raw parts of Lloyd's burned mouth like lemon juice on an open wound. He winced and nearly choked as she rounded his lower bedpost.

Inches from his torso, she stopped, stared at him for an agonizing moment and said, "Try and get some sleep."

Holding back his gagging he answered, "I will."

She stood back and stared at him for what felt like ages, then stepped back and left the ward, leaving him with a burning mouth full of deodorant, but with great-smelling breath.

Lloyd wasn't surprised when he returned from class the next day and found his bed moved again.

FIFTEEN

HOCKEY PUCKS AND IRREVERENT CLANSMEN

That which restrains us from what we want to do
will often dictate what we truly want to do.

Merriam-Webster defines incontinence as the "inability of the body to control the evacuative functions of urination or defecation."

Incontinence plagued Lloyd every day. Repeated hospital stays following the shooting did little to alleviate his hygienic insecurity. Whatever form of incontinence he experienced in an institution was easily cleaned up and resolved by the nursing staff. By contrast, his episodes of incontinence within public spectrums were almost endless streams of embarrassments. As he grew older and more aware, he was under constant scrutiny with noticeable stains on his clothing. His keen sense of awareness and sharp hearing made it that much worse to overhear brands of "foul smelling" and "stinky."

It wasn't just his inability to control his bodily functions. If he could keep whatever he excreted confined to his under-garments that would have been fine. It was when the discharge involved those around him that he became that much more horrified. For many, it's easy to understand why they decide never to leave the sanctity of home.

A common scenario outside of a hospital setting was: he'd be standing there trying to speak to someone intelligently, and without warning, a flow of urine would start its water-board torture drip down his pants. Because of his lack of control and loss of feeling, he wouldn't be aware of the trickle forming a lake of unfathomable proportions on the floor surrounding him. The lake wouldn't confine its borders to the tips of his shoes, but expand beyond to the shoes of those around him. People quite literally had to lift their pant-legs and tiptoe (or run) away from him while stepping around the pool, leaving him drowning in abject horror.

Or Lloyd might be standing there talking to some gorgeous number he had designs to woo, and a huge turd of Gibraltar dimensions would roll from its comfortable roost in his underwear, down the inside leg of his pants, careening off each corner of his brace, leaving tiny, almost indiscernible traces of residue to find or most certainly smell later. Now, after a short time, the mound may have decided to slow its progress down the leg, resting on the inside or outside of his thigh, giving the impression of a sudden outgrowth, warning the prospective partner that he was more excited about them than even they could imagine, and depending on the trajectory of the roll and its position of rest, more well-endowed than even he could imagine.

Public incontinence provided an almost endless stream of embarrassments.

Try as the prospective partner might to ignore the distraction, while Lloyd remained oblivious and continued his witty banter, they and others witnessed the mound creating what appeared to be an avalanche flowing down his leg. The bulge would worm its way slowly down below his knees, then, plopping with its accompanying *flop* sound, the rock would rest between Lloyd's feet. Or, even more horrifying, the boulder may continue its inexorable roll off the contours of his shoe, hitting and bouncing off the edge of the shoe of the prospective partner or another hapless individual standing close by. At this point, no one in his vicinity was immune to becoming the next croquet stake!

Once free of the layers of clothing, and in full view, people with such disabilities learn to kick their stool to obscure regions of a room. Becoming an accomplished hockey player is only a minor lesson of incontinence. There are much more subtle occurrences that rarely go unnoticed.

There is an almost constant fragrance of urine or feces that surrounds and follows people afflicted with paralysis and those suffering levels of incontinence like *Peanut's* Pigpen's cloud. As a result, they often exaggerate their use of cologne and deodorant. A caregiver or close friend will often lean into the ear of the individual and whisper, "You're ripe!" But being enveloped in a smell makes one immune to it. The old phrase states, "A fox never smells its own hole."

The mental scarring as a result of incontinence, and its accompanying smells, develops overnight. Even within controlled environments, no one escapes subtle forms of prejudice. In public, such expressions of prejudice become that much more overt. When a person is young and normally impressionable, occurrences of incontinence cause nearly overwhelming embarrassment. Add any additional sensitivity to the mix and very easily, phobias and overcompensating ticks develop the likes of which a team of Freuds would have a lifetime's pleasure to unravel.

> *Phobias develop, the likes of which a team of Freuds would have a lifetime's pleasure to unravel.*

Spinal cord impingement is still a nebulous science. Everyone with traumatic paralysis suffers varying degrees of damage, replete with a unique degree of physical repercussions elsewhere in the body. There is rarely clear demarcation of damage, no distinct line by which you can determine if an individual will have bowel, urinary control, or sexual function. If the paralysis is higher, add to those complications breathing and the inability to swallow effectively.

Lloyd's spinal cord was severed completely at the twelfth thoracic vertebrae level. He had little to no control of his bowel or urinary functions. And as he was left with no sexual function, his greatest distraction from total despondency was his bursting internal desire to please women. But, despite the distractions, a growing resentment continued to thwart his every move.

The nurses thought that by moving Lloyd's bed they could keep a closer eye on him and possibly quell some of his internal angst. There is little doubt they thought that his growing anger could infect younger members of the ward. They were not entirely oblivious to the levels of frustration prevalent in all wards.

A Sister from the local Catholic Church was commissioned by the powers that be to come in to speak to the patients. They assembled seven of the oldest and more aggressive of Ward 14 in the playroom. Lloyd was among them.

The woman was high-spirited, young, and demure in her long black robes with white forehead band. Sister Angelica immediately went to work. Without addressing the group, she methodically set up a small portable record player she brought with her. She turned, facing them, and began to sway side to side in time with the music. The boys listened and watched with bewilderment as she stood there, eyes closed, rocking back and forth to the sound of Simon and Garfunkel's, "I Am a Rock."

She implored their undivided attention. "Please, just listen to the lyrics."

The import was too obvious. A couple of them were not as kind to hide their eye rolling.

After a short pause, she continued, never slowing her sway. "You'll notice they sing, '*I am a rock, I am an island.*' What do you think *I am a rock* means?"

She perused the room, picking out those she assumed were more responsible. She pointed to Jerry Gates.

"Hey, it's a song, lady! Who gives a shit?"

She immediately jumped on that statement. "Oh, please don't use profanity in your answer."

Jerry laughed loudly.

Lloyd smiled. He knew this was just another in a long line of futile attempts by the administration, and in particular Miss Laux, to extinguish patients' growing hostility.

Lloyd spoke up. "Could I ask you a question?"

"Yes, you may."

"Why would someone so beautiful be a Nun?" The comment was accompanied with a series of "ooooohs" from the group.

She blushed. "Okay, why did I become a Nun?"

Ignoring the "someone so beautiful" comment, she continued. "I became a Sister of the Catholic faith because of my love of our Lord, Jesus Christ."

Lloyd wouldn't let it go. "Did you date anyone before entering your faith?"

"Well, I had a date or two."

A voice in the back of the room shouted, "But you didn't have sex, did you?" It was Yack.

Though her cheeks were almost totally obscured by her uniform, she exhibited an obvious blush. She was determined and hid, as best she could, her discomfort. "I find that question highly irregular. But, to answer it honestly, I'd have to admit that I did not have sexual relations with anyone prior to entering the Faith."

The group was gripped with her honesty, shocked that she would even answer such a question. But, while knocked off guard, Lloyd knew he couldn't let her off the hook.

"How 'bout we make a deal? You answer our questions, we answer yours."

She was game. "I've been honest with you so far."

Spinner spoke up. Spinner was Bill Durant, whom the boys had nicknamed after Frankie Avalon's character from *Beach Blanket Bingo*. Spinner was thin, but another tough kid from northern Pennsylvania. He had been in hospitals since the age of three for trouble with his legs and had just recently transferred to E-town.

Spinner pulled no punches. "Hey, don't you feel like a woman?"

"Of course I do!"

"Then, won't you say you must have de same, uh... how should I say dis?" He scratched his chin. "...Uh, *urges* every woman has?"

Yack chimed in. "Yeah, we like dem urges!" Everybody laughed.

She didn't have a clue where this was leading. Clearly, it wasn't going as expected. "...Y-yes."

Spinner continued. "Den, how 'bout a date?"

Everyone broke up laughing.

She was clearly embarrassed. "You people are nothing but a group of scofflaws!"

With that, the laughter burst into complete mayhem. A few guys started to spin their wheelchairs. Others cracked their crutches against bedposts. Those confined to beds or stretchers slapped their rubber mattresses.

Yack sneered. "Oh no, we're nothin' but a bunch of scofflaws!" It started a chant. "We're nothin' but scofflaws! We're nothin' but scofflaws! We're nothin' but scofflaws!"

Sister Angelica lost control and hurriedly gathered her things, putting away her record and little record player. No one noticed her exit as she disappeared out of the playroom because they were having too good a time.

Scofflaw became their new favorite word for the next six months, and though not one of them could even tell you what the word meant, they deduced that it was derogatory, and to a man, they were happy to wear that name as a badge of honor.

Sixteen

TRAINING AND A SURPRISE VISIT

*More often than not, when we venture beyond our
comfort zone, we are surprised to note even greater
comfort in the new zone.*

According to UCSF Medical Center, "Bladder training is an important form of behavior therapy that can be effective in treating urinary incontinence. The goals are to increase the amount of time between emptying your bladder and the amount of fluids your bladder can hold. It also can diminish leakage and the sense of urgency associated with the problem. Bladder training requires following a fixed voiding schedule, whether or not you feel the urge to urinate."

Lloyd tried a number of times to train his bladder. He had no "urges," and he had no care-provider to monitor his progress. By pressing down on his abdomen above his bladder, to force emptying it, in half-hour intervals, each attempt failed with accompanying misery and embarrassment. Doctors convinced him to surrender and have urostomy surgery at Coatesville Hospital in Coatesville, Pennsylvania.

Clinimed.co states:

*"A urostomy is a surgical procedure which diverts the
normal flow of urine from the kidneys and ureters into
a specially created stoma. To create the stoma the
surgeon will isolate a short piece of your small intestine
from which he will fashion a tube or spout (known as
an ileal conduit). The two ureters will be plumbed into*

this spout which will be brought to the surface of the abdomen. Urine will continue to pass through the stoma, completely bypassing the bladder."

Yack had the surgery and his experience with it was unadulterated freedom. "Oh, you're gonna love it, Ace! You get there and they don't give a shit what you do. The first five minutes I was there, I bought a pack and smoked the whole time. It was great!"

Lloyd had to ask, "How was the surgery?"

Yack leaned back in his chair. "Fuck, the surgery's nothin'. They put you to sleep, you wake up, and it's all over. No problem. Wait 'til you see the women!"

Information regarding Lloyd's prognosis and even his current diagnosis was sparse and in spite of his increased empowerment, still hard to come by.

It was midsummer 1966, and with the decision having already been made for him, he was informed only two days before admission for his urostomy surgery. His first clue was Mrs. Gipe's insistence he drink a tall glass of Castor Oil, followed by x-rays to determine the clarity of his bowel.

One of the nurses brought the glass to him.

"You expect me to drink this?"

"Mrs. Gipe told me to be sure and watch that you drank every drop."

"Every drop, huh?"

"Please don't get me in trouble, Lloyd! Mrs. Gipe told me to watch you."

"All right, all right."

It was a tall glass, at least two cups worth. He stared at it for a moment and realized the longer he waited, the harder it would be to down the swill.

Others in the ward were watching him and comments were beginning to flow.

"Oh, how disgusting!"

"Don't drink it, you'll puke!"

Lloyd just smiled. Someone was always watching. And he loved the attention. Without further hesitation, he touched the glass to his lips and gulped it down with impassioned eagerness. He drained the glass and the contents hit his stomach with a thud.

The aftertaste was horrific, a mixture of grease and the faint hint of citrus they mixed it with to keep it palatable. He ate a small packet of saltines in an attempt to disguise the phlegm, but it wasn't long before the effects of the drink engineered its inevitable push. It partially accomplished its intended purpose.

Lloyd was much too thin to even consider sitting on a steel bedpan. The accompanying blowout was not minimal, however, his x-rays continued to show residue in his bowel.

Mrs. Gipe ordered enemas to follow the Castor Oil, round after round, and as she did, his strength weakened with each successive regime and their explosive aftermath. He was not popular that day.

An x-ray was ordered after every third interval, and results were not favorable. After five intervals (that's fifteen glasses of oil and enemas!) he still wasn't cleaned out enough to meet the minimum preparation for the surgery.

Mrs. Gipe called it quits. Lloyd was much too depleted to continue. It was at the end of the day when he was ready to crawl under the covers of his bed that he received word of a surprise visitor.

Lloyd was told there was some emergency, and his brother Bink was waiting to see him.

Lloyd was already on a stretcher, having been transported to and from the tub room where he was bathed after a series of blowouts. Lloyd was told there was some emergency, and that his brother Bink was waiting to see him in the playroom.

This was strange on a few levels. For one thing, it was in the middle of the week and visiting hours were only on Saturday and Sunday afternoons. Another thing was that he hadn't seen Bink in years, well before his admission to E-town, and knew the chance of Bink's being released from the Air Force and visiting was extremely remote.

One of the nurses informed Lloyd. His response was immediate. "You're kidding! Where is he?"

"No, I'm not kidding. He says he's your brother and he's in the playroom. I'll take you."

As she pushed his stretcher toward the playroom in his stuporous state, Lloyd's mind cycled the possible reasons for the visit.

As the stretcher rounded the corner, Lloyd could see his brother in the far corner eyeing the turntable. He was tall and thin.

Bink turned. He looked excited to see his brother. "Hey kid, great stereo system you got there."

Lloyd smiled. "Yeah, we like the big speakers."

"They look like they can crank out some real volume."

He nodded toward the nurse. "Thank you." She turned and walked out.

Bink then reached down, wrapped his arms around Lloyd and kissed him firmly on the lips.

He looked drawn and haggard, as though he had ridden through the night without much sleep. His clothes, what there were of them—scruffy jeans, a t-shirt and a thin leather jacket— were tattered. He grabbed a chair and slid it as close to Lloyd's stretcher as he could. He smelled of gas and smoke.

Road-worn, he sat uncomfortably, as though in pain. "How you doin', kid?" His face was expressionless; he was trying to prolong the conversation.

"I'm okay. What's goin' on? They told me there was an emergency. Is everything all right?"

Bink stood up, kissed Lloyd on the forehead, rubbed his forearms and sat again leaning forward. "You're getting stronger. Your arms are really filling out."

Lloyd was pleased his brother noticed. "Yeah. I've been lifting weights."

Bink paused, held Lloyd's hands and slowly leaned back again. He looked away then stared deeply into Lloyd's eyes. "What I have to tell you may not make much sense to you, but it has to be done and you're the only one that can do it."

Lloyd was puzzled. "I thought you were in the Air Force. What happened and what's the emergency?"

He seemed cross. "Don't worry about the Force. A Sergeant was riding me hard and I decked 'im. They threw me in the brig and finally discharged me. But that's not important."

This all came as a shock to Lloyd, but it still did not constitute an emergency.

After a brief silence, Bink continued. "What I have to say I can only say to you. You're the only one that can understand."

He was still holding Lloyd's hands and Lloyd was growing more anxious with each passing moment. Lloyd couldn't get over how disheveled his brother looked.

Bink sat up. "I just rolled in from Dakota on my bike. It's outside." He smiled and looked away. "I wish I could take you for a ride. You'd love it." He then leaned back again and with tears full, looked down.

Lloyd was concerned and pulled on his brother's hand. "What's goin' on, Bink? Talk to me, man."

Bink leaned forward and reached behind his back. When he drew his hand forward he was holding a knife. "Do you know what this is?"

Lloyd knew exactly what it was. A few of the guys would bring them from home. Lloyd had even won one in a poker game and held it for a few weeks before the nurses confiscated it. "It's a switchblade," Lloyd blurted.

Lloyd took it from his brother. It was white with pearl inlay. He pushed the button on the bottom and flipped the blade. It wasn't long, but long enough to do some damage. The blade was sharp though and Lloyd could feel it had a good handgrip. He knew that was important in a knife fight. He pressed the button and adeptly snapped the blade closed.

Bink was surprised his little brother had learned to handle it so well. "You've had some education in here."

"I used to own one."

Bink grabbed Lloyd's arm, the one with the switchblade. With Lloyd holding it, Bink reached back, pressed the button again and flicked the blade out of its sheath, to its fullest extension. His eyes were bloodshot and still full of tears. Holding Lloyd's arm, with the blade extended toward Bink's chest, not looking at the knife, his body began to tremble with each word.

> *Bink grabbed Lloyd's arm, the one with the switchblade.*

"I've been thinking a lot about what you've been through... what I put you through. I know you're tough, and you can take a lot. You've taken a lot because of me... me shooting you. I can never get that out of my mind." His tremors increased. Tears started streaming down his cheeks. He drew himself closer as Lloyd held the knife. His respiration increased.

Lloyd could tell there was desperation. "Bink..."

"No, don't speak! I can't sleep. I can't eat. All I think about is the shooting and what I put you through." He grabbed Lloyd's right arm, the knife extended. Slowly, he began pulling Lloyd's arm and the knife closer to himself.

Lloyd could surmise what was happening. With his already sapped strength and compromised thinking, Lloyd felt as though he were leaving his body and viewing a macabre scene from above his stretcher.

Bink could easily have leaned into the protruding spear. He may have even been able to twist Lloyd's hand upward and, on any angle, lay himself onto the blade. In all cases all Lloyd could have surmised was that it would have ended in a botched mess. Despite whatever damage may have occurred, Bink could still have been successfully resuscitated.

As his thoughts raced, not all scenarios were perceivable to Lloyd. What became crystal clear to him though was Bink's intent. He wanted to die, and he wanted Lloyd to be the instrument of his death.

"I want you to end it. I want you to end this nightmare!"

Bink pulled harder, but diminished as Lloyd's strength was, it held. As though aided by a supernatural force, his arm locked.

Bink was outraged. "Do it, Lloydie! Do it! End it!"

Lloyd started crying, but Bink insisted. "Stick me, Lloydie! Stick me! End it!"

Lloyd could smell his brother's breath on his face, urging him on. He knew this was wrong. What frightened him at the start, now spurred him to anger. Finally, clarity and compassion overwhelmed him. "Stop it, Bink! No one's dyin' today! I love you, man! You will not die by my hands!"

The words struck. Bink looked up as though he had been slapped across the face. His grip was strong, but Lloyd held firm.

Bink stood up and tugged once more, but as he looked deep into his brother's eyes, he could see the resolve. Finally, after what seemed like the ultimate tug of war, he relaxed his pull. Exhausted, he leaned forward and they embraced.

With a flick of his wrist, Lloyd pressed the button on the knife and returned the blade to its cradle. Crying, they held each other for what seemed like an eternity.

It was only a few minutes before the head nurse came in and informed Bink that he could come back during normal visiting hours, but that he had to leave now. They broke their embrace and as he wiped the tears from his face, Bink smiled at his little brother. Hidden from view, Bink pocketed the knife.

"You're tough, kid!"

"I love you, Bink."

He smiled again. "I love you too, Lloydie."

Bink looked up at the nurse and back at his brother. Holding Lloyd's head in his hands, he kissed him hard on the forehead.

"I'll see you around."

He started to drift out of the room. Before leaving, he turned to look at his brother one last time. "Take care, kid."

Watching his brother's tattered leather jacket turn the corner, Lloyd only nodded.

Seventeen

SURGERY AND THE BIG FIGHT

"Your reputation precedes you." —Origin Unknown

When he arrived at Coatesville Hospital, the nurses escorted Lloyd to the main adult ward. Anyone beyond 12 years of age was considered too old for pediatrics. Lloyd felt like a kid in a candy store. The world was his oyster.

A pack of cigarettes was his first request. He smoked a few, of course, but what was of particular interest to him was his discovery of the hospital's policy on conjugal visits. He noticed immediately that when wives arrived, adjacent ward mates pulled their curtains closed. Lying there, a cigarette in one hand, a Coke in the other, flimsy curtains closed around him and he soaked in all the accompanying sounds. Just listening was entertainment enough.

Prep for any surgery is laborious. Lloyd endured the relentless series of enemas. The Coatesville nursing staff were meticulous in the scrubbing and shaving of his body. The surgery was not only flawless, it was uneventful. Dr. Uhlman, the urologist, had done so many urinary diversions it was as routine a process to him as picking up his morning paper.

Lloyd spent three days in Coatesville and did his best to flex his newfound freedom muscles. The first day was spent smoking cigarettes, drinking a beer, and swearing openly. The second day was the surgery and recovery. The third day was a blur. Still recovering and sensing his eventual return to the Children's Hospital, his mood was considerably more subdued.

There are various routines associated with the urinary diversion's maintenance. Lloyd was relieved that the nursing staff cared for every aspect of the new protrusion of flesh they referred to as his "stoma." What little he was taught was that the stoma had to be digitally dilated on a regular basis, or it would heal closed.

Attaching a urine-collection pouch to the abdomen in 1967 was a painstaking, messy process. The stoma is the outward protuberance of the bowel, from which an internal bladder was created and urine flow continues unabated. The skin around the stoma had to be thoroughly dry before attaching an appliance. A clean absorbent pad placed over the stoma acted as an effective wick. The obvious purpose was to absorb as much of the draining urine as possible while prepping the area.

Once dry, the ringed area was then coated with an eighth-inch thick glue, an inch and a half in circumference. Again, it was critical that the glued area remain free of moisture long enough to apply the thick rubber pouch. One tiny drop of moisture anywhere on the glued surface, and with the watertight seal compromised, urine formed a channel and its inexorable march to leak out. This forced the staff to reverse the process and begin the application anew. Once compromised, the skin had to be cleansed of excess glue with a caustic product that irritated (a severe burning sensation was often reported) and smelled like flammable petroleum. The process was maddening.

The drainage bags, thick rubber devices, had a raised circular disc at the top that surrounded the stoma and attached to the skin using double-sided glued wafers and thick paste. This process was replayed at least once every few days. There were often instances when Lloyd had to have his appliance changed numerous times in one day. The thick rubber appliances were reused over and over, so to clean them, nurses soaked all urinary drainage bags in a communal vinegar bath. There is little wonder many patients suffered recurrent urinary and kidney infections as a result.

As unceremonious as his return was, being thrust back into the simmering cauldron of Ward 14 was disconcerting. Now he felt more vulnerable with a new wound on his abdomen. In an environment growing more aggressive by the day, he knew the first thing an opponent would do is attack his most vulnerable spot. Getting hit in the stomach could send him into a tailspin of pain and serious physical injury.

> *As unceremonious as his return was, Lloyd felt more vulnerable with a new wound on his abdomen.*

In his absence, Yack had been consolidating his power and was ready to make more moves against Lloyd and Bob, so Lloyd was sure to remain on his abdomen during the day and sleep on his back at night.

While happy to be "home" again with his boys, Lloyd did miss his brief taste of freedom. It was the fall of 1966 and the air was getting cooler. Gary Muller had been released from isolation, and had taken up residence in the center of the ward. When he saw Lloyd enter, Gary waved to him.

"Where's your guitar?" Lloyd asked.

Gary smirked and shrugged his shoulders. "I broke it."

This didn't surprise Lloyd. While he was being assisted onto his bed he asked, "How?"

Gary snickered. "I threw the damn thing!"

Anxious to assimilate as quickly as possible, Lloyd positioned himself in the center of his bed and Bob and Spinner moved across the ward to greet him. They were a welcome sight.

"Hey guys, how the hell are ya?"

They both returned a "Hey" in unison.

Spinner leaned closer. "Mrs. Gipe told Gary to bathe one morning so he threw a basin of water at her. She got pissed, took out her bucket of cold water and threw it back at him. He picked up his guitar, chucked it at her, missed her, and it smashed in a million pieces against the door. He's such a fuckin' asshole!"

Bob continued. "He's been fightin' with Harvey, too."

Lloyd was intrigued. Harvey Scholt was a member of the Amish community. Harvey and Lloyd had become quick friends when they were paired in the same cubicle some months ago. He'd told Lloyd on numerous occasions that his father insisted that he had to leave school after the eighth grade to work the farm, as was the custom for Amish males.

Harvey lived with dwarfism and stood only 4'6". He moved with the agility of a gazelle in bed, and if he had to, he could grab you like a python and, holding you like a vice, pound you to a pulp. Lloyd's vow to always be honest with him was enough to cement their immediate friendship. Despite having to cope with a great deal of intolerance at home, Harvey fit right in to the ward mentality, always going out of his way to help kids whenever possible, mending fences in some volatile situations. He was one of the most peace loving, non-combative people Lloyd had ever known. It didn't make sense to hear that Harvey was actually fighting someone.

"You mean, Gary's givin' Harvey a hard time?"

Spinner broke in. "They go at it, fists and all! Harvey's kicked his ass a coupla times."

Lloyd was astonished. He knew Harvey was powerful, but Gary was a pretty big kid. He also knew Harvey would do all he could not to fight with someone. "You're shittin' me!"

Bob was more insistent. "No shit, bro. They go at it."

Lloyd smiled. "What sets Harvey off about 'im?"

Bob shrugged. "Shit, Gary smacks his ol' lady, man! It don't take much to get people pissed off at 'im."

Lloyd smiled. "I gotta see this!"

Spinner smiled, too. "You'll see dat an' me kick his ass, too! I hate de son-of-a-bitch, ever since I saw him swing at Jonette!"

"Jonette? Who's Jonette?"

Spinner had a half smile on his face, obviously embarrassed.

Bob leaned over and said, "She's one of the maids."

Spinner added, "She's cute, too!"

Lloyd said, "She new? What happened to Maggie?"

Spinner said, "Dey shipped her out to anutter floor. Upstairs, I think."

Lloyd would miss Maggie, but kept that information to himself, "Oh, I get it."

"Hey, Ace! What's shakin'?" The voice was familiar.

"Yack. How are ya, man?"

"I'm good. How was the surgery?"

"It was all right."

"Yeah, but did-ja get laid?"

"No, but I did pinch a beautiful ass," Lloyd lied, but it got a reaction from Spinner and Bob.

"Yo, there ya go!"

Yack leaned back in his chair. "Yeah, I'll bet it was an orderly!" Yack could always better someone with his quick wit.

Spinner and Bob reeled. "Oh!"

Yack had done his damage. "Well, I guess I'll leave ya to get settled with your little flunkies here." With that, he pulled his wheelchair around and wheeled off.

Bob was quick to respond. "Whoa, who's a flunky, fuck-face?"

Yack just laughed.

Bob, watching Yack wheel away, leaned into Lloyd. "Man, we gotta pound him bad!"

Lloyd just sighed. "I had my chance to pound him, just didn't pull the trigger."

Bob said, "I won't have any trouble pulling the trigger."

Spinner also leaned in. "Yeah, Yack's been buggin' Bob, too! He's been callin' him out!"

"Yack callin' Bob out?" Lloyd looked at Bob.

Bob smashed his right fist into his left hand palm. "Oh, it's gonna happen, bro! It's gonna happen!"

Lloyd smiled. "Well, if it's gonna happen, let's make it happen."

Bob smiled. He didn't know what Lloyd's plan was, but he trusted him.

Lloyd didn't actually have a plan, but he didn't need one. He knew if he badgered Yack enough, he could goad him into fighting with Bob and Yack could finally get the punishment he deserved at the hands of someone who would only be too eager to give it to him.

> *Lloyd knew if he badgered Yack enough, he could goad him into fighting with Bob.*

The next morning, Lloyd called over to Yack, "I got a bone to pick with you, *Ace!*"

Yack was only too eager to oblige, "Anytime, Ace!"

"How 'bout when I get back from class, lunchtime?"

"Great. Anytime you say."

Lloyd had a particularly difficult time with his classroom studies that day. Miss Oberholtzer was in a real tiff over his inability to grasp Latin declensions, but that wasn't all. With his rolling up the sleeves of his t-shirt (hiding that from Miss Laux, the Director of Nursing, of course), slicking his hair back with Brylcreem, his overuse of colognes, and his chronic failure to complete his homework on time, Miss Oberholtzer's patience with him was wearing thin. Despite his outward appearance and deteriorating attitude, he remained respectful toward her. His mindset was in a completely different direction however. He questioned everything and his education was at the lowest rung of his priorities.

Yack was waiting for him when Lloyd returned to the ward. "So, you got a bone to pick with me, Ace?"

Lloyd tried to ignore him, but that was futile. When the nurse walked away to assist someone else, he said, "Yeah, let's talk."

Yack wheeled closer.

Lloyd leaned down and whispered, "You've been givin' Bob shit?"

Yack leaned back and shrugged it off. "So, what of it?"

"You really think you can kick Bob's ass?" Lloyd was almost pleading with him to wake up from his delusion.

Yack was undeterred. "Sure. Why not?"

"Why not? Because he'll fuckin' break your fuckin' neck, that's why!"

Yack started to laugh.

"And he'll use what neck you have to shove it up your stupid fuckin' ass, that's why!"

"Wow. You really like this fuck, don't you? The guy's a shit-farmer! I'll show him how much shit he can kick, when I kick his ass!"

"I'm trying to save your fucking life!"

"Don't worry 'bout me. You'll see who's in charge when I kick his ass!"

Lloyd just stared at him for a minute, smiling.

Yack broke the silence. "What?"

"If you really want this, let's do it." With that, Lloyd called over Bob.

Yack grew uneasy. Bob stood over Yack's head, behind his wheelchair. Yack spun around and said, "Hey, let's do this right!"

Bob grabbed a chair, and turning it backwards, set it right in front of Yack, then leaned into his face and said, "How do you want to do this thing?"

Yack was surprised and noticeably uneasy. "Uh, well, the first thing, we have to be sitting next to each other when we start. No one standing!"

"Great. What else? Do you want me to tie one arm behind my back? I'll do it!"

Yack kept his eyes on Bob. "No... you don't have to."

Lloyd loved this. It was quiet as each warrior stared at the other.

Finally Lloyd broke the silence. "We'll do it on Saturday, so there's not so many people around, when the nurses are on lunch break."

Both Yack and Bob agreed. Bob extended his hand to shake on the terms. They shook on it. Bob stood up and said, "Good! Let's do this!"

Saturday was upon them. The morning was quiet, as was the ward after lunch when most of the staff took their break. All of the guys were aware of what was to take place and gathered around Lloyd's bed.

Lloyd and Bob were ready and only too willing to stage the fight, but positioning all the wheelchairs to give optimum view for others was a test in logistics for Lloyd.

The fight had to occur in chairs—Yack in his wheelchair, Bob in a regular chair. Both fighters were right-handed, so chairs had to be positioned facing each other in a staggered side-by-side configuration.

Yack wheeled over and pulled up facing Bob in his chair. They shook hands and smiled at each other.

Yack looked at Lloyd and asked, "Okay, how we gonna get this started?"

Lloyd said, "Just start by taking turns punching each other on the shoulder. But remember, Bob. No punches below the chest."

Bob said, "Okay, who goes first?"

Lloyd said, "Yack, you go first."

Yack said, "Okay." With that, Yack leaned forward and lightly tapped Bob on his right shoulder with his right fist. Bob, in turn, leaned forward and punched Yack a little harder on his right shoulder.

They continued to trade shots back and forth until Bob, exasperated, leaned back in his chair and said, "Are we gonna keep playin' this patty cake shit, or what?"

With that, Yack leaned forward and slammed a hard right into Bob's chest, pushing him back. Bob immediately leapt forward with a hard shot of his own, and the melee was on.

They began trading shots when Bob swung wide and hit Yack hard in the midsection just north of his sternum. The shot pushed Yack hard against the back of his chair. As Lloyd watched Yack's eyes roll back into his head, his compassion for his old friend emerged and he grabbed Bob's shoulders and pulled him back into his chair.

> *Lloyd reached for Yack, who was barely breathing. He couldn't help his old friend.*

Lloyd reached for Yack, who was barely breathing. He pulled Yack forward and slapped him hard in the face. With no response, he started shaking him.

Now, Lloyd was scared. He couldn't help his old friend. Suddenly, just as the thought occurred to him that maybe his friend could die, Yack spit up and started coughing. Gasping for air, spitting saliva and choking, Yack was in bad shape.

Lloyd told Ronnie, "Get a nurse, quick!"

Lloyd pulled Yack closer to him and unbuttoned his shirt. By the time the nurse arrived, Yack was already beginning to revive. Gradually, he could catch some air and began to breathe normally.

The nurse looked at Lloyd and asked, "What happened here?"

Lloyd answered, "Yack sneezed and started choking."

She poured a glass of water, leaned closer to Yack and handed it to him. "Leonard, is that correct?"

Still unable to speak, Yack took the glass from her and poured it over his head, then coughed and with his left arm waved her off with an affirmative nod.

She stood more erect and stared at him, then carefully surveyed each of the boys. "Well, all right. If you're sure that's all there was to it."

Yack's face was red and bloated, eyes wet with tears from choking and snot running out of his nose. He whispered, "Yeah. I'll be fine."

The remainder of the group remained in place and breathed a sigh of relief. The fight was over, the crisis averted.

Eighteen

XMAS PARTY

"No bird soars in a calm." —Wilber Wright

Furloughs were being awarded for a five-day period from Dec. 23 to 28. Since Lloyd was continually passed over, negotiating for a chance of enjoying one became his primary objective. Whichever physician walked through the ward, he, along with others, was on them at every step.

Each patient had their own, but this was Lloyd's mantra: "Come on, Doc! My sores are healed, I passed the surgery for my bag and I can take care of myself. I'll come back in one piece!"

The doctors' obvious reluctance to let Lloyd go home was that they would probably spend the next year patching him back up, if he even made it back alive. Their fears were not unfounded.

At that time, orthopedic residents were required to perform a six-month rotation at E-town. They performed surgeries under the supervision of an established orthopedic surgeon. Like all rotations, their appearance was generally ragged and they were always in dire need of an extra hour of sleep.

In passing, Lloyd called to one on night duty. "Hey, Doc. Could we talk for a minute?"

The resident, laden with a stack of patient charts, hesitated. He knew one simple affirmation could turn into a major conflict so he had been warned to be careful about offering assistance without approval of the immediate director or Miss Laux.

But this was an opportunity to get off his feet without being further badgered by the nurses, so he pulled up a chair and sat down. As he did, he put most of the charts on top of Lloyd's cabinet and rested his feet on the edge of Lloyd's bed, flipping open one of the charts.

"Sure. I have some charting to do, but what's on your mind, Lloyd?"

"I was wondering why the hold-up on my furlough approval?"

The resident leaned back in the chair and thumbed through the chart. When he reached the page he needed, he withdrew his pen and started writing.

The doctors' reluctance to let Lloyd go home was that they would probably spend the next year patching him back up.

"There's a lot of things to consider before they let you waltz on out of here."

"What things? It's only five days!"

The man was growing exasperated. "Well, to start with, there's the trouble with your decubitus ulcers."

"What trouble? They're healed."

"That's just it. They *are* healed. And we want them to stay that way."

"They'll stay that way. What else?"

The doctor closed one chart then opened another, readjusting himself in his seat.

"You also have a few other things to worry about. You're not out of the woods yet on a lot of issues."

"What issues?"

"You're still healing from your urinary diversion."

"I move around all right."

"Sure, and while you remain in bed or on a stretcher, you're fine. Can we be sure you'll remain in bed or on a stretcher in your home?"

"What could happen?"

"What could happen? Well, the great suture work that's been done could be reversed."

Lloyd was amazed to hear this. "You mean I could actually rip open those old sutures?"

"Not only rip them open, but tear a gaping hole in much of what is now your buttocks. You could literally bleed to death before reaching a hospital."

Their fears were not unfounded.

"Okay, I'll be careful."

"But there's more."

"How much more?"

"Well, you know you're scheduled for back surgery soon."

"Yes, I heard."

"We want you in top-notch shape for that."

"Okay. Anything else? This is a lot of stuff."

"I know. But it's important you understand our trepidation about sending you home."

"I get it." He leaned closer to the doctor. "You know, Doc, it's been over four years since I've seen my mother."

The doctor agreed. This was the only time his attention veered from a chart. "I know how hard that must be for you, Lloyd."

"Is there anything else I have to worry about?"

The man grabbed another chart. "Well, we don't want you to worry, but you should be careful if you do go home."

"Anything else?"

"You've been in bed for a long time."

"Yeah, tell me about it!"

"Do you understand what happens to your bones when they don't have pressure placed on them for an extended period of time?"

"What happens?"

"They develop a chronic disease with the loss of calcium called osteoporosis."

"Osteo...*what?*"

"Osteoporosis. Your bones become brittle, like Swiss cheese, and they can break easily."

"How 'bout if I take some calcium? Can I reverse the effect?"

"It would take years to reverse a process that took years to develop."

Lloyd bowed his head against his pillow.

"Okay, I get it. I'll be careful. Please, let me go home!"

The doctor rose, grabbed the chair, and put it back in its place. Reaching down and picking up the stack of charts, the conversation was now done. "We'll see. Think about what I said."

"I will. Thanks."

Tension continued to build, but there was one shining glimmer of hope left before the end of the year, if only for a few days, most guys... *including Lloyd*... were finally going home! For some who had not had the pleasure of going home on a regular basis, or at all, the holidays took on a whole other level of importance.

If only for a few days, most guys... including Lloyd... were finally going home!

Christmas trees were placed strategically around the nurse's lobby area and the back ward. Guys in the front ward were denied a tree for being branded "too rowdy." Both wards were on high alert the night of Dec. 22, 1966, and when the nurses finally turned out the lights, murmurings of dissent were in the air. No one slept and there were already multiple warnings from the staff to, "Settle down, or else!"

One newbie, Jake Bauer, was a photography freak, always shooting people in compromising positions. Jake was going home for the holidays and had been told he would be discharged in a few weeks. Jake had nothing to lose that evening. He had a spool of fine thread that he tossed across the fairway of the ward to Harvey, whose bed was opposite his.

He whispered, "Tie an end to the bottom rail of your bed and send it back."

Harvey responded quickly by crawling to the bottom of his bed, tied one end of the thread to the bottom of the bedpost, let out a few feet of thread and then tossed the spool back to Jake.

Jake took his stainless steel drinking cup (all were issued a stainless steel bedpan, urinal, washbasin, and drinking cup) and taped it to his small camera, being careful to position the flashbulb at the very center of the drinking cup. He then carefully positioned the items on the lower left side of his bedpost, pointed upward at a 45-degree angle toward the center of the fairway.

He took the thread that Harvey threw back to him, looped it around the right corner of his upper bedpost, measured the length, cut the thread, and tied the end to the shutter button of the camera, being careful to keep the thread taut across the center fairway.

The evening supervisor was a hefty woman.

The evening supervisor was a hefty woman. Recruited by Miss Laux, she was seasoned and close to retirement. Annoyed that she had to respond to the staff nurse's complaints about patient unrest that night, she moved slowly. She had already made one walk through the ward earlier. With the increased chatter and repeated warnings to settle down, another trip was inevitable.

It wasn't long after Jake had set up his flash unit that she made her return. Most of the patients were attentive to Jake's set-up. When they heard her footsteps, all settled back to see what would happen.

When she reached Jake's bed, all eyes were riveted on her face, then just as she was about to pass, a huge *flash* lit up the entire ward. The light was so blinding those watching on the backside of the cup were amazed at its brilliance.

Ironically, the woman was entirely unmoved by the antic. Unflappable, she continued in her stride, straight to the nurse's desk.

Well before she exited the room, patients sat straight up in their beds in total disbelief. No one could imagine such control under so bright a light.

Jake said, "Did you see that, Harv?"

Harvey, undaunted, said, "I'll get 'er!"

The entire ward was anxious to see Harvey's plan.

He called to Jake. "Tie the end of the thread to your upper bedpost and send it back." Jake did it, and threw it over to Harvey. Harvey tied his end and sent it back to Jake. This was repeated several times before Harvey tied his end last and chucked the spool back to Jake.

Everyone watched as Harvey and Jake set the trap. There wasn't any elaborate camera work this time. It was just a group of fine threads expected to block the night supervisor's passage.

The boys didn't have to wait too long before the woman began the sojourn back to her office.

The slapping sound of thick leather nursing shoes against the polished linoleum piqued everyone's interest. All remained quiet to see what would happen. She was obviously unruffled by the previous flash as she picked up the pace through the ward. She held her clipboard to her side and looked straight ahead as she approached Harvey and Jake's bed. Strolling along casually, she reached the outside edges of each bed.

As she progressed, there was a visible indent beginning to form against her chest. Her pace slowed, but she leaned forward and powered on. She wore a bulky white uniform that extended well below her knees. And despite her ironclad bra and heavily starched blouse, the compression by the thread became more visible as the threads reached their breaking point. Just as it seemed as though she were bound and her forward progress stopped, the threads released en masse.

SNAP!

Her whole body lurched forward and she took an extra step just to stand upright. She caught her balance, and stood there in silence, looking down and behind her to see if there were any loose floor tiles. She stroked her breasts and thighs, trying desperately to determine the cause of the phantom weight. A few snorts and even fake farts could be heard throughout the ward. She felt nothing, and in the dark, couldn't see the dangling broken thread on the bedposts. She stood motionless, then looked skyward, as though the answer could have come from the almighty.

> *Her whole body lurched forward.*

After endless moments, she gathered herself, straightened her blouse and her hair, and continued on down the hall. She wasn't thirty feet beyond the ward before the entire floor erupted in laughter.

Bob and Lloyd, separated by a few beds, reveled in Harvey and Jake's latest maneuver and carried on about what they looked forward to accomplishing while home. Similar conversations were being held throughout the front and back wards.

Bob and Lloyd were talking when Lloyd's speech was broken by a shadowy figure seeking refuge under his bed. "What the fuck?"

"Sorry, Lloyd. I'm Larry Bremewitz from the back ward!" His speech was pressured, and he was panting.

Lloyd didn't know the boy, but that didn't matter. His reputation preceded him. "What's goin' on?"

"All hell's breakin' loose in the back. We didn't like the cheap Christmas tree they gave us, so we started chuckin' the balls around. They explode like bombs when you hit something!"

Just then, another figure ducked out of sight under his bed.

The first guy, Larry, spoke to the new figure. "Ace, you gotta go back!"

The other kid, also unknown to Lloyd, answered, "What? Whattiya fuckin' mean, I gotta go back?"

"You gotta go back and get my specs!"

I'm not goin' back there now! Fuck that, man! You know what it took to get this far. I ain't goin' back!"

Just listening, Lloyd knew the kid was right. The fact that they were able to make it from the back Ward 16 to the front Ward 14 was an amazing feat in itself. The guys had to traverse at least fifty yards with very little cover, an open area encompassing the nurse's desk and three on-duty nurses!

The first boy, Larry, spoke again. "I gotta have my specs, man! I can't see wit-out 'em!"

The second said, "Fuck!" but snapped to attention and slipped out of sight, back into the light in the direction of the nurse's station.

Lloyd was amazed at the second's obedience. It wasn't long before the entire front ward was fully awake and aware of the intrusion.

When the second kid returned, many in the ward were impressed with his nimble agility and congratulated him with cheers and applause.

The kid bowed. "Thank you for your support." He spoke as though he were a reporter in a war zone. "They're really battling it out back there. Balls are flying all over the place. Someone got wild and threw a couple at the nurses. They smashed a couple against the door. The nurses don't know what to do!"

The news started to liven up the fully awake Ward 14. Lloyd had a basket of gourds gathered that afternoon from the lobby and they were being tossed around. The place was turning into a free-for-all.

Bob crawled out of his bed, resigning his bid for sleep, and pulled up a chair next to Lloyd to witness what was going on.

Spinner appeared to Lloyd out of the darkness and whispered, "Hey man, Gary Muller is lying on his side with his balls hanging out. Let me have one of those gourds." Lloyd passed it over and Spinner was gone.

As usual, Gary, the unabashed flamboyant, never spared the ward a "show." There he was languishing on his side in his hip-spica—a type of plaster that covers both legs from the ankles up to the level of the belly button. An area around the groin is cut out for toileting.

> *Gary's jewels were in full view of patients and staff.*

Gary's jewels were in full view of patients and staff. He had been warned for weeks, amid taunts and jeers to "cover up" or the guys would police him themselves. The guys whose beds were closest and had to look at that all day every day had it out for him. Some of the staff, despite numerous pleas, could not compel Gary to act with more decency, and quietly requested that Lloyd try to reason with him.

Gourds were beginning to bounce off the walls and some metal bedposts surrounding Gary's cubicle. Lloyd and Bob saw Spinner moving closer to Gary. It was just a matter of time.

Lloyd asked Spinner if he needed more gourds, but Spinner whispered, "I'll only need one."

Lloyd and Bob watched as Spinner cradled his gourd like a football. Rather than wing it from a distance as others had done, he bent down and crawled along the floor to Gary's bed-stand area. They were impressed with his stealth.

Ironically, with all that was going on, and even the gourds that barely missed him, Gary was still fast asleep, his legs splayed openly. Spinner was out to change that in a hurry.

As Spinner rose up on his knees, there was just enough light for the others to see him cock his arm, eye his target, and throw dead-aim right into Gary's private package. Where the other gourds landed hard against metal and plaster, the one Spinner threw hit like a hard punch into a soft catcher's mitt.

Lloyd heard a dull *thump*.

Gary's cries were muffled at first, and then increased to a loud wail to alert the nurses. "Eeeeoooooooooooooowwww!" He screamed in pain, crying and swearing uncontrollably, his list of cursed epithets against the staff, the hospital, and especially Spinner.

Rather than quell the onslaught against him by alerting the staff, Gary's histrionic outburst provided the necessary fuel for Spinner's already fired hostility. He started to slap Gary across the face, hard, almost in an attempt to snap him out of his madness.

Gary's short fuse and hot temper compelled him to lunge at Spinner with a fierce thrusting left hook that took Spinner by surprise and almost knocked him to the floor.

Gary continued his flail, but Spinner dodged and ducked and avoided the throws altogether. Gary's attempted punches were so intense that his upper body weight, his missed swings and momentum carried him and his heavy cast right off the bed, smashing his body, cast and all, on the hard linoleum floor.

This was followed by another more guttural scream. "Oww!"

Everyone else cheered.

With that, the nurses rushed in and flicked on the overhead spotlights.

The head nurse yelled, "All right, what's going on in here?"

Gary, flopping on the floor like a fish out of water, had his entire bed ripped apart. The pillows and sheets were pulled off and thrown in obscure parts of the ward. His mattress was literally standing beside his bedside, where he had grabbed it to shield himself from Spinner's onslaught. He was flailing so wildly he'd pushed his entire bed to the center lane of the ward.

Spinner now stood over Gary and laughed hysterically. When the edge of one of Gary's casted legs brushed against one of Spinner's casted feet, this was the added catalyst (as though he needed one) that prompted Spinner to dive down and start pounding Gary's head in.

The entire ward cheered in unison. "Yeah! Yeah! Yeah! Get 'im, get 'im, get 'im!"

The head nurse, listening to the rally, realized the futility of trying to restore order, and so turned around, walked out, and went straight for the phone.

Bob turned to Lloyd and said, "She's calling security."

"So what?" Lloyd said. "What can they do?"

Bob looked worried. "Yeah, but they could start crackin' heads!"

Lloyd was adamant. "They're not gonna crack heads. They don't take us seriously enough as it is. We're only kids to them."

Lloyd knew better. These "kids" were a powerful force. He was a strong believer that people, however young, however disabled, deserved respect and pushed too far were an unstoppable force. He also knew that when you intentionally keep people from frequent visits with their loved ones, and then restrict social activities, you're pouring increasing amounts of salt on already deeply engorged wounds.

It was after 10:00 and all the lights of both wards were fully lit. Nurses scurried back and forth in futile attempts to reason with the patients. As the night wore on they found it increasingly difficult to squelch fights and salvage the destruction of property, not to mention the obvious damage patients were doing to themselves, the casts and splints they were breaking and the results of surgeries they were jeopardizing.

In less than an hour, a few nurses who had given up sat in the corner and just cried.

By the time the security guard arrived with the night supervisor, Gary and Spinner were trading blows in the middle of the ward. The remainder of the boys surrounded the two combatants and cheered. From the perspective of those outside the immediate circle, it was a major title fight that no one could stop.

The crowd cheered every shot Spinner could land in hopes that something would compel Gary to wake up and adhere to some semblance of hygienic decency. And the crowd's wishes were being answered.

Gary's clumsy attempts to ward off Spinner's attack were failing miserably. And with every failed attempt, Spinner became even more empowered, beating Gary handily.

Lloyd, eyes fixed on Spinner's onslaught, didn't see the security guard and night supervisor enter the ward. He was too concerned with Spinner's zealousness, and whether Gary would be able to hold his own.

Bob saw the guard though and touched Lloyd's arm to direct his attention. Slowly most of the kids began to notice the stout figure standing erect at the end of the ward. Everyone, including some of the nurses, were surprised that the unkempt, bearded, heavy-set individual elected to protect them, was so old. The man looked well into his seventies and moved with the spunk of a turtle.

When he began to step between the two pugilists, the night supervisor, an elderly woman herself, grabbed his arm and stated, "Let them get it out of their system!"

She knew Gary's history, was well aware of his foul mouth and obnoxious behavior, and was only too pleased to see his comeuppance at the hands of an equal.

> *The night supervisor was only too pleased to see Gary's comeuppance.*

Spinner, still pummeling Gary, noticed that his actions were now sanctioned by the "authority" and became even more energized to finish the job.

Lloyd watched intently. When he was sure Gary had had enough, he yelled, "Spinner!" Seeing no reaction, he yelled again, louder this time. "Spinner!"

The second shout quieted the crowd.

Spinner stood tall, and stopped punching Gary.

"That's enough!"

Spinner's head rose just high enough to see Lloyd over the haphazardly flung bedsheets and now dispirited onlookers. The ward was clearly out of the control of the staff.

Spinner yelled back, "Lloyd, if you want me to stop, I will."

A few in the crowd yelled, "Come on, man! Let 'em fight!"

Spinner would often ask Lloyd, while pounding on someone, if he thought his victim had enough. There were times when Lloyd would say, "Give 'im one more shot. That should do it!" In this case, with everything in full view of the staff, Lloyd thought he'd be a little more magnanimous and relieve Gary of further punishment.

The room grew silent as everyone's attention turned to Lloyd. He was resolved. "He's had enough."

Spinner, bloodstained, nodded in agreement and casually stepped away from the still flailing, wailing Gary on the floor.

The night supervisor and guard attempted to help Gary back to his bed. He was still out of his head, swearing uncontrollably. "You fuckin' people aren't helping me here! You fuckin' people don't give a shit about me! You fuckin' people just don't give a shit!"

The supervisor and guard's disgust was palpable as they assisted him.

The supervisor continued trying to reason with him. "You needn't use such harsh language, Gary!"

Gary would not be quieted. "Listen to me, bitch! You don't get it! You people just don't give a fuck about me!"

The night supervisor escorted the guard out while Gary continued his stream of curses that was enough to make the elderly woman's hair curl.

"You fuckin' bastards are goin' to get sued. I'll sue the shit out of all of you fucks! You fuckin' people don't protect anybody, you just let people fuck everyone up. He could've killed me!"

It was after 11:00 and there still wasn't a scintilla of evidence that the group was satisfied and ready for sleep. After the supervisor and the guard left, staff nurses worked their way through the ward, picking up errant gourds, ripped sheets, and pillow cases. As they did, they issued repeated warnings to be quiet and settle down. The warnings fell on highly agitated, deaf ears.

Spinner worked his way back to Lloyd's bed to proudly display his war wounds. Despite overt dominance over Gary, he was marred with bloody scratches and marks.

Out of breath, he said, "I got 'im, bro!" Spinner flopped back into his wheelchair in utter exhaustion.

Lloyd patted him on the shoulder. "Good job, good job!"

The lights were extinguished, but the boys continued speaking openly. Everyone was awake and talking. There was little doubt in the nurses' minds. These people were not about to nod off to sleep too soon.

After repeated admonitions, the staff nurse motioned to call the night supervisor again. The flood lights were lit in sequence in preparation for her arrival. As the abundant light enveloped the darkness at the far end, a gaunt figure could be seen standing at the entrance. All of 5'6", armed in one hand with her clipboard and her glasses dangling from the other, it was six hours before her next shift and she was the physical embodiment of utter despair.

Amid the groans of Yack and his crew, "Hey man, we're tryin' to sleep here!" the woman stood as a statue.

Her voice barely rose above a whisper. "You may think..."

Although her first few words were inaudible, lost within the din, quietly, almost imperceptibly unruffled, she started again.

"You may think... that since you are going home tomorrow, you are automatically exempt from receiving punishment as a result of your behavior tonight. Well, allow me to disabuse you of that notion."

They understood "abuse," but they didn't quite get what "disabuse" meant.

She stopped to acknowledge how very silent the room had become and then continued. "If this ward is not quiet within five minutes, you all will have a week's grounding added on to the two you've already been grounded for!" Her voice rose in volume to a screech. Again, this was met with groans and the all too familiar "clicks" of the tongue on the upper palate to express disapproval from Miss Laux, the Director of Nursing.

The lights were summarily turned out, the evening shift left, and the night shift came on. Miss Laux sauntered to the nurse's desk to inform the staff that despite lingering grumbling, they had the resources to quiet the raucous group. She insisted that everything was "under control."

She knew that all the people she hired lived their lives in total regimentation, if not in their private life, most certainly in their professional life. She could guarantee that every aspect of care, through each shift, was set up in routines engineered by her and executed by nurses such as Mrs. Gipe on all floors. Every head nurse working Wards 14 or 16 feared Mrs. Gipe and adhered to her methods, tried and true as they were, of discipline with absolute allegiance to her and Miss Laux.

Patients enduring those routines, day after day, week after week, year after year, were well aware of the backlash they would receive from any form of reprisal. The prospect of someone finding cracks in those routines, and exploiting them for their own pleasure, were very low. And although scheduled fights were handled more privately, the sheer art of those patients mobile enough to exploit flaws and gaps in the nurses' routines, either for themselves or others' benefits, was nothing short of genius. Those courageous few could obtain food, drinks, and even cavort with equal, if not more adept stealth the patients of the opposite sex from apposing wards.

The repercussions from getting "caught" sneaking around, darting between shadows to acquire goods and visit people, were more than simple reprimands. Some kids who were found floating around at night were ordered or forced back to their bed. Some were restrained and drugged to keep them there. Others were found so recalcitrant they were drugged and then discharged outright to their family, never to return.

Singularly, antics occurred all the time, certainly more frequently than most administrators would admit. But this event was unusual on many levels. The boys were still excited, fully awake and moving freely. The evening staff was only too eager to relinquish the group to the next shift. Their night was over. To the night staff, the nightmare was just beginning.

Talking continued and the night nurse warned patients again. "I promise you, gentlemen—no... *babies!* You want to act like babies, I'll treat you like babies! If I have to, I'll move every bed in this ward and park each one of you in front of Miss Laux's office if I hear one more peep out of ya!"

> *To the night staff, the nightmare was just beginning.*

Her comments were met with the usual moans and groans.

She screamed, "I mean it!"

As mentioned, there were very few pleas allowed from patients to doctors. Whatever changes in protocol doctors tried to make, Mildred Laux could easily squelch with the unlimited power yielded her by the Medical Director, Dr. Saunderson. Patients refused to adhere to old notions of "speak only when spoken to" and "do as I tell you to do without question."

Tension increased as the patients of Wards 14 and 16 collectively committed to one objective—upset the system and upset it tonight!

Most continued their discussions and planning. Joel Hooker came up with a marvelous idea about Rudolph, the red-nosed reindeer. He crawled out of his bed, and weaved his way under and around beds to avoid being seen by the nurses. Slithering on his hands and knees to one of the large glass doors of the porch, he leapt through and easily reached the stereo in the playroom with its big speakers.

He quietly and methodically combed through a half dozen record boxes in the dark. Among all the stacks he reviewed, he selected Burl Ives' version of "Rudolph the Red-nosed Reindeer." Being careful not to get caught, he placed the record on the turntable, cranked the volume, and dropped the needle on the record at the farthest point on the edge of the vinyl with plenty of time to race back to his bed before the music began.

At 12:30 AM the stage was set for Rudolph.

"Now there's Dasher and Dancer, Prancer and Vixen..."

The volume was so loud it could be heard in the next county! Wards at the opposite end of the institution had no problem making out every word of that wondrous tune.

"...Comet and Cupid, Donner and Blitzen. But do you recall, the most famous reindeer of all?"

The lights of the ward flicked on again and younger nurses were dispatched to the playroom. "Turn that racket off!"

"...Rudolph the red-nosed reindeer... had a very shiny nose. And if you ever saw it..."

Scraaaaaaaaaaaaaaaatchchchchchchchchchchch!

The staff member who reached the stereo first created the terrible sound of someone taking a needle off a record via every groove.

Kids cheered in a chorus. The guttural explosion emanating from the speakers was the perfect punctuation to the evening. And, although the lights were extinguished for the umpteenth time, the evening was not quite over.

Amid all the hysterics, exaggerated laughter, and celebration, the leaping in and out of their beds, throwing their pillows, relishing the triumphant defeat of the "establishment," the group barely noticed the silhouette of a tall figure standing within their midst.

Before them, almost as though the ghost of Christmas past had called him, "Mr. Scrooge" suddenly appeared in full bedtime regalia, his one-piece pajama, open ankle-length raincoat, with sleep hat dangling at his side no less. It was the administrator of the hospital, Dr. Saunderson!

The odd aspect about his sudden appearance was that his presence held very little significance to many of the half-crazed teenagers. Most didn't have a clue who was standing before them.

Almost as though the ghost of Christmas past had called him, "Mr. Scrooge" suddenly appeared in full bedtime regalia.

Whispers of, "Who the fuck is this guy?" could be heard throughout the ward. "What is he, another security guard?"

As word trickled throughout and his identification was established, the boys slowly quieted and showed a bit more restraint, although there were still a few who could not simmer down.

Standing in all his monarchical, wrinkled bed-wear, God spoke. "Now, gentlemen. Everyone's tired. I'm tired, the nurses are tired."

He spoke as though delivering a homily, with a smooth undertone, almost out of earshot to those furthest from him. He was calm, although quite visibly shaken by the evening's festivities. A few wondered when he mentioned that the nurses were tired, whether he was concerned the night-shift people would be losing valuable sleep while on duty.

"I want no further outbursts such as this the remainder of the evening."

Short and sweet, clear and concise. Right to the point. There was a long silence as though the words were of such magnitude that all present needed time to ponder their import.

He bowed his head out of exhaustion and started for the nurse's desk. Only his shuffling footsteps could be heard as the huge monolith in his long trench coat, like Count Dracula's cape flowing behind him, worked his way slowly toward the light.

The huge vacuum created in the wake of his departure sucked all the oxygen from the room. The "Count" spoke briefly with the nurses at the desk then disappeared down the back stairs.

The vacuum was effective. With the exception of a smattering few, the boys were exhausted, rolled over, and fell fast asleep.

NINETEEN

HOMELIFE

"We leave something of ourselves behind when we leave a place. We stay there even though we go away. And there are things in us that we can find again only by going back there. We travel to ourselves when we go to a place that we have covered, a stretch of our life, no matter how brief it may have been."

—Amadeu, in *Night Train to Lisbon*

L loyd's brother, Bink, picked him up the next morning with his red '65 Ford Mustang. Exhausted from the night before, Lloyd leapt onto the stretcher. When they brought him out, Bink wrapped Lloyd in a thick blanket and gingerly lifted him into the back of the hatchback. Traveling the long distance from Elizabethtown to Edison, New Jersey, a three-hour drive, would give the boys ample time to catch up on the years lost.

Their mother Lillian, along with their two sisters, Rhea and JoAnn, greeted them warmly when they arrived. Lloyd's mother lived with her husband Joe in a modest two-story house they rented on the edge of a 500-acre estate near Rt. 287 in rural Edison. Joe planted a half-acre of vegetables every summer, much of which was canned by Lillian. Lillian worked part-time as a waitress at a local restaurant. Joe was a bull-dozer operator in the summer months. He liked to hunt deer in winter.

Lloyd's mother was a passionate, inviting individual. Beset with the loss of three children at a very early stage of her first marriage, and then the subsequent incident of Lloyd getting shot, tragedy seemed to follow her like the plague. When her remaining three children were taken from her, shortly after Lloyd's shooting, she moved around for years trying desperately to find suitable work and a homestead in the fervent hope of regaining custody.

With the exception of a few sparse weekends, mostly major holidays, she rarely saw her children. After years of searching, she met and fell in love with Joe. Settled, she began to reassemble her family. Lloyd, at the Children's Hospital, was the one child she saw the least. Now, after nearly five years apart, they were to be reunited.

Lloyd's mother always had a remarkable ability to cook. His fond memories of her had served him well. His mouth was watering well before his brother carried him into the kitchen from the car.

Their sobbing mother wrapped her arms around both as they entered. Lloyd's tears started to flow as he inhaled her strong perfume and the roast in the oven. His mother was determined to cook all of their favorite meals, and although the house was foreign to both of them, familiar smells along with the sight of their family together again, enveloped them like a warm blanket.

Christmas day was extra special. Lloyd's mother had planned everything from soup to nuts.

Christmas day was extra special. Lloyd's mother had planned everything from soup to nuts. They all woke up early, opened their gifts, and then settled in for a hearty hunter's breakfast. Hunter's breakfast was a staple in the Negoescu tradition. Generally intended for breakfast, it is an egg dish, mixed with potatoes, green pepper, and onion, covered with cheese.

Out of earshot and beyond the view of their mother or Joe, the boys physically wrestled, perhaps to regain what was taken from them in their years apart. Both agreed that the brief encounter they had a few months earlier was not what either had envisioned a brotherly reunion should be, but neither spoke of the meeting. Lloyd was still conflicted by the event and wondered whether his brother was stable psychologically. He was also clear in his desire to assert his new level of independence and prove his superiority over his domineering older brother.

It had only been seven years since the shooting. To say that it was difficult for Lloyd's mother and sisters to accept Bink back into the fold would put it mildly. Strained as it was, the family made a valiant effort to include him over the holiday. Much to the bewilderment of his loved ones, Lloyd was happy to see his brother and help alleviate his developed anxieties.

He had also just come from an environment in which he was asserting greater control with remarkable effectiveness. It was working for him on the ward, so why shouldn't it work for him in the real world?

His brother had other ideas though, and they struggled each day they were together. While Bink, acting the older brother, wanted to instill strength and assertiveness in his younger protégé, he was surprised to note his younger brother's relentless challenge to his authority.

It would start as Lloyd's topping his brother's comments with his quick wit. Bink never appreciated being challenged, and these encounters, as fraught with layers of conflicts as they were, were no different.

The day after Christmas, his mother took the girls shopping to buy ornaments at a reduced price. While they were away, Bink and Lloyd continued acting out their pent-up frustrations.

After a particularly snide remark, Bink jumped on top of his brother to pin him down. Lloyd was able to hold him at bay and continued to wrestle. When he'd had enough, Lloyd pushed his brother off of him.

When Bink fell back he landed on Lloyd's thighs. Both heard a muffled *SNAP!*

It wasn't long before Lloyd fell violently ill. He flopped to one side and his brother noticed something was wrong. "Lloydie, are you alright?"

"No." Lloyd's voice was clear but shaky. "My... my... stomach!"

"Your stomach? Is it your, the bag thing?"

"No... I don't think so... I don't know." Lloyd recoiled as if to throw up, but stretched out straight, holding his abdomen.

Bink stood up, wrapped his arms around his little brother's legs and back, then lifted him off the floor and proceeded to carry him to his second-story bedroom. He laid him carefully on the bed and began exploring what could be the probable cause of Lloyd's distress.

He probed with his fingers around Lloyd's hands. "Does this hurt?"

"No."

Bink continued his exploration around Lloyd's chest. "How 'bout this?"

"No."

Lloyd was getting cold and his body began to quake.

Bink said, "You're shaking. What's goin' on?"

Lloyd could barely answer. "I... I... I... I don't know."

Bink covered his brother with a blanket, while still trying to figure out what was wrong. He checked Lloyd from head to toe. Carefully eyeing Lloyd's extremities, he gently squeezed and moved each leg. Lloyd's left thigh didn't seem quite right to him. There appeared to be an extra joint that extended above the knee and below the hip.

> *Lloyd's left thigh didn't seem quite right...*

Something was strange and Bink knew it had to be addressed as soon as possible. Without a word, he hastily covered Lloyd in blankets and raced downstairs.

Lloyd's mother had just returned with the girls from shopping and was preparing the night's meal when Bink met her in the kitchen.

"Mom, I have to get Lloydie back to the hospital. He's starting to run a fever!"

"What's wrong? He was fine today."

Bink was hesitant to provide too much information. "You know how he is. His condition is always on the edge. He probably got another urinary tract infection."

Bink left her and went out to the car to prepare the back hatch area for Lloyd.

He then went in through the kitchen where his mother stopped him. "Can we take him to a local hospital, so he can stay closer to me and I can visit him?"

Bink was frantic. "Mom, the people at the Children's Hospital know him. They know what he needs. We have to get him back to that hospital as soon as possible!"

"All right, I'll make some sandwiches for you."

Lloyd was shivering briskly under a stack of blankets when Bink entered the room. "Lloydie, we have to get you back to the hospital."

Lloyd tried to be adamant. "I'll be all right. Just let me rest a little."

Bink was even more forceful as he quickly packed Lloyd's medications and small clothing bag. "No, we have to go. This is serious!"

Lloyd resisted, but only minimally, as his brother wrapped him and his meager belongings in blankets and carried him down the stairs. His younger sisters, Rhea and JoAnn, met them at the bottom and each kissed Lloyd as Bink carried him to the kitchen. Their mother was already in tears.

Presenting them with a small paper bag she said, "I made you something you like. I love you, my darlings." She wrapped her arms around both boys.

Lloyd, already sweating profusely, cried too as his brother completed the trip to the back of the Mustang.

His mother watched from the open kitchen door as Bink gingerly placed Lloyd in the vehicle. As they sped off, neither Lloyd nor his mother could be sure if they would ever see each other again.

TWENTY

CAST LIFE AND GAMBLING

Periodic and consistent distractions
are a healthy respite for the mind.

The drive back to the hospital was quiet. In the throes of a 101-degree fever, Lloyd shivered under a pile of blankets in the rear of the Mustang. He couldn't eat, and his stomach was upset. His brother kept the pedal to the metal, avoiding police traps along the way.

When they finally arrived, it was early in the evening. Bink hastily carried him into the building and dispatched him onto a nearby gurney like an overdue package. Because they had arrived so late, the main lobby was empty. Bink wheeled his brother to the boy's ward, tracked down a nurse, informed her that Lloyd was sick, then kissed his brother and promptly walked out.

Only a resident was on duty that night to assess the damage. It was confirmed after an x-ray that there was a clean break to Lloyd's left femur. After some hand wringing for sanctioning him the furlough in the first place, the doctor plastered him in a hip-spica cast and escorted him back to the ward.

Lloyd's friends, seeing him return in plaster, greeted him like a conquering Roman hero.

Spinner met him first. "Hey, Ace. What de hell happened to you?"

Before he could answer, Lloyd was gratified by how fast his crew surrounded him. Ronny and Lurch gathered with the circle to hear the tale. Bob's absence was conspicuous.

Lloyd had time to formulate a story, and considering his audience, he knew he'd have to make it salacious. "You're not going to believe this, but it's true, and I feel stupid even now. Where's Bob?"

Spinner spoke up. "Nobody knows anything."

Lloyd was perplexed. "What does that mean?"

> *Lloyd knew he'd have to make the story salacious.*

Ronnie jumped in. "He went home and that was the last we saw of him."

Lloyd asked, "Did he stay home? He loved the farm."

Spinner said, "Nobody knows."

Ronnie spoke again. "What happened to you?"

They all leaned in to hear the details.

"Well, my brother took me out to a bar. And these days it doesn't take me too long to get wasted. Well, there I am checkin' out some chicks sittin' around, when one of 'em comes over and sits right next to me!"

He looked around and everyone was leaning in to hear more.

"We're talkin' and drinkin', and then she says she wants to go to the bathroom. She gets up to leave. As she does, I reach out to touch her arm. She moves too fast, and I miss her completely and that's when I go down like a ton a bricks."

Lurch yelled, "Oh, no!"

Lloyd continued. "Oh, yeah! Like a ton o' bricks!" He leaned back. "Yeah, so I'm layin' there, laughin' my ass off. People start crowdin' aroun', and I'm thinkin', fuck, how de hell am I gonna get off this floor?"

Everybody laughed.

"My leg's all twisted up underneath me. I don't know what de hell's goin' on. So, I look up and see all these people starin' at me, and all of a sudden, my brother breaks through and kneels down next to me. 'You all right, Lloydie?' he says. 'Yeah, I'm all right. Just get me de fuck off this floor!'"

More laughter.

Spinner said, "What 'bout that chick? Did she help?"

"Nah, she was outta there, like I had de plague or somethin'."

Ronnie said, "Man, you didn't even get some tail!"

Lloyd shrugged. "Tell me 'bout it, shit! Anyway, my brother picks me up and we head home. My mom was pissed 'cause I was three sheets to the wind. She gave my brother shit for takin' me out. Then, that night I start runnin' fevers and here we are!"

Lurch leaned forward in his wheelchair. In his quiet voice he said, "You fucked up, man!"

Everybody busted out laughing.

When the laughter died down, Spinner gave him the grave news. "They're shippin' us out."

Lloyd looked at him with a scrunched face. "Whattaya mean, they're shippin' us out?"

"We're all goin' upstairs to the new Ward 20."

Lloyd looked around for someone else to shed light on the issue and settled on Ron. "What's goin' on?"

Ron pulled his wheelchair up. "They're almost done workin' on the new ward upstairs, and gonna move us all up there. But they say it's air-conditioned and shit. I don't know. I don't like it!"

Lloyd was incredulous. "What de fuck?"

Spinner moved closer. "Yeah, they're gonna split us all up, in different rooms. I'll be stuck wit all de retards from 16."

That comment didn't sit too well with Ronnie, who was a member of the Ward 16 tribe. "Hey, man!"

Spinner, realizing his gaffe said, "Oh, sorry!"

Lloyd stretched his neck out. "They're mixin' us up with the guys from the back ward?"

Ronnie chimed in, "They're puttin' us all together."

Lloyd couldn't believe it. "How de hell are they gonna do that? They have that much room up there?"

Ronnie was clear. "Yeah, it's a pretty big area they're puttin' us in."

Patients became more subdued and withdrawn as word spread that there was going to be a "move." To an individual, they were unsure what lay before them. They knew their surroundings would be forever changed. How that would pan out and in what form it would take were daunting questions for them.

There were strict instructions laid down by Miss Laux to all staff that no one was to describe or attempt to describe the new wards. Patients were not allowed to step foot or have any access to the new surroundings. Doors and elevators were locked and sealed when construction halted at the end of each day. Even those more mobile could not breach the locked areas of the new ward.

Patients could see the endless stream of workmen as they paraded past. And although there were a few construction workers who would acknowledge the patients with a nod or wave, they were forbidden to socialize in any way.

The constant parade. A few days passed when Lloyd was shocked to see two men escorting someone through the ward. As they neared his bed, he had to say something to halt their progress. "Wait, guys. Bob, is that you?"

The group stopped. Shabbily dressed, Lloyd could barely recognize his disheveled friend. Bob barely stood as he teetered between the two men. Lloyd could see that without their assistance, Bob would have collapsed. In a smiling groggy voice he said, "Hey, man..."

"Bob, what happened?"

"Hey man, wha' happen to you?"

"Oh this? I fell off a bar stool while on furlough. No really, Bob. What de hell happened to *you*, man?"

"Oh man, I couldn't take it anymore..." His voice trailed off as though he were asleep on his feet. The men stabilized him and shook him a little.

Bob continued. "I went home. You know how much I miss it..."

Lloyd said, "Yeah, I know."

"Well, I gothh home and den it was shtime to come back... and I din't wanto... but, my dad made me! He made me! When he drop me off here, I shaid to myshelf, man... I ain't hangin' here no more!"

Lloyd was anxious. The guys wanted to go to wherever they were instructed to take Bob. "Bob, what happened to you, man?"

"Hey, when my da drop me off, I di not wanta shtay here. Sho, I took off, man! I shplit, man! They picked me up five milesh from here... and when we got back, dey shtarted shootin' some shit in ma veins. Now, der draggin' me outta here."

Lloyd was depressed. "I'm sorry to hear that, Bob."

Bob was cool. "Hey, ish no prob, man. I'm cool. Hey, you take care now... and get de hell outta here, man!"

Lloyd answered, "I will sooner or later."

Bob leaned down, gave Lloyd the American Indian arm shake, and with the assistance of the other two, walked out.

Lloyd watched as Bob strolled down the hall with the other men. With a tear in his eye, he wondered, without his dear friend, how much harder life could become.

With a tear in his eye, he wondered how much harder life could become.

Waiting, with no idea what their future entailed, was maddening. Many patients were sad that their groups would be disbanded, others were certain that conditions would be much worse than those they were already enduring.

Time passed slower on the ward, sans his friendship with Bob. The weather grew warmer in the summer of 1967. All of the patients, in varying conditions of impairment, were aware that they would have to deal with the impending heat. Those in casts were not pleased and could only grumble that their fate would be far worse. There were a few who, despite the fact that they were without casts and ambulatory, argued that their condition was so unique they could not tolerate the heat and would suffer more as a result.

All would be impacted and uncomfortable, but most accepted their lot and soldiered on. Lloyd had endured the stifling effects in the confines of his isolation room, and was convinced being out in the ward, while no cakewalk, was far better.

What he particularly enjoyed were the marathon poker games that occurred in the playroom. Distractions from unbearable conditions are always helpful. Playing board games, for people in bed, was their preferred distraction. As patients aged, despite their financial standing, the desire to make money was paramount so, gambling gained in popularity that summer.

Although the playroom was an open area with wide doors on opposite sides, unless staff stood within the room they could only check on the patients with frequent walk-bys. Patients enjoyed greater freedom knowing the staff was stretched to capacity.

It wasn't unusual to see four wheelchairs, four beds and stretchers and three guys on crutches in seats squeezed between them, surrounding the playroom's makeshift table. Acey-Deucey was the preferred poker game.

Players would ante up. Two cards were dealt face-up to one player. That player then bet whether or not the third card would numerically fall in between the first two. If the third card fell in between the two other cards, the bettor took the amount he bet out of the pot. If the third card fell outside of that range, the bettor must add what he bet to the pot.

Acey-Deucey was the preferred poker game.

The boys' version was that those dealt two Aces had to declare one Ace "high" and one Ace "low" and could only bet based upon his own available cash. If the pot was $15 and the player wanted to bet "The Pot," he had to have the available cash to cover it. Play continued until the pot had been cleared.

The ante was cheap enough. All fifteen players put in 10 cents to fill the pot to $1.50, which was more money than seventy percent of them could handle.

Yack bet 75 cents on his King-2 combination. He drew a 2 though, and had to dummy up his 75 cents amid the "ooh's" and "ahhs" of the other players. This almost broke him.

Two guys either had a pair (two of a kind), or cards too close in proximity to bet (an 8 and 6, or a 5 and 2), so they relinquished their cards.

With Yack's loss, the pot was now $2.25. Two of the more financially elite of the group had good "split" cards, with a distance of rank between them, and bet "the pot."

Remarkably, they both lost and the pot grew to a whopping $10. What appeared to many as easy bets had turned costly.

Two guys bet smaller amounts and lost, bringing the pot total to $15.

When the time came for Lloyd to bet, he wasn't feeling very confident. He drew an Ace-2. He had the $15 to cover an "all in" bet, but that was it. He knew that if he bet "the pot" and lost, he'd be dead broke.

> *Lloyd knew if he bet "the pot" and lost, he'd be dead broke.*

With each loss, players who had to "dummy up" grew much more vocal and rebellious. Each succeeding loss brought cheers and jeers. Now they were even louder and more boisterous.

"Bet the pot! Bet the pot! Bet the pot!"

Lloyd laughed, but felt pressured. Having the grand split, the vast rank difference between the Ace and 2 was more than enough to spur him to action.

First things first. He called, "Ace high." To emphasize what he meant, he raised his index finger and stated again, "I'm callin' Ace high."

Everyone knew what that meant. He was betting that any card between the Ace and 2 would be a winner for him. He could safely draw a 3, 4, 5, 6, 7, 8, 9, 10, Jack, Queen, or King. However, drawing another Ace or 2 would prove fatal.

The other guys were collaborating on what cards had already been played to determine what cards remained in the deck. Two 2s and one Ace had already been played, so with Lloyd's Ace and 2, there was only one more 2 and two more Aces yet to be declared.

It was now time for Lloyd to declare his bet. The chants for "Bet the pot!" reached a fevered pitch.

When Lloyd raised his index finger for the second time, the room fell silent.

Spinner, who had been sitting on the edge of Lloyd's bed, was an ardent non-gambler. He stated many times, "I hate to lose. I only bet on things I know I can win." Spinner leaned over and whispered, "Don't bet, man! The table's cold!"

When Lloyd raised his index finger for the second time, the room fell silent.

Yack overheard the admonition and said, "Don't listen to him, Ace. You're a big boy now!"

Lloyd just stared straight ahead. He knew what this involved. And he wasn't about to let an opportunity like making fifteen bucks walk away. Plus, he had great cards!

"I bet..." He paused for effect. "...the pot!"

The room erupted in cheers and laughter.

"You can do it!"

"You're gonna bust!"

Yack was quick to speak up again. "Put the full fifteen bucks on the deck, Ace!"

Lloyd responded with, "Calm down, Yack. No sweat." He drew out his wallet, counted fifteen singles, and put them on the table. He said, "No problem."

The dealer held the deck in silence, waiting for the din to die down. No one wanted noise to notify the staff.

Spinner yelled, "Shut up, you assholes! You'll get the whole fuckin' suits on our backs!"

Everyone settled, all eyes on Lloyd and the dealer. Would he bust, or would he walk... well, *wheel*... away with a cool fifteen bucks?

The dealer pulled the card and slapped it on the table.

The dealer pulled the card and slapped it on the table in front of Lloyd.

It was a 2.

The entire room erupted again.

Lloyd just looked dumbfounded, his gaze transfixed on the card.

Yack was quick to pounce. Laughing, he said, "You bit the big one this time, Ace! Pay up!"

Without speaking, embarrassed that he'd lost in such a humiliating way in front of the entire ward—and especially in front of his old nemesis, Yack—picked up the $15 and threw the money in the pot.

The next kid in line held a 7-King split, bet the pot, and cleaned it up with a 9. That kid won a cool thirty bucks!

With that, the entire room disbursed for the night.

Lloyd had already been informed that his curvature of the spine would be addressed in the coming months. This added to the already growing apprehension of his impending transfer to the new Ward 20 and his recent $15 "sting" at the poker table. To replenish his bankroll, he learned that there was real money in acquiring baseball cards, and that the guys from Ward 16 had developed games involving them. This reminded him of a talent he acquired in isolation—the ability to pitch cards.

While in isolation, he'd used his deck of cards to accurately hit objects at the other end of his bed. Hours spent holding one corner of a normal playing card and tossing it at an object a few feet away could pay off, he thought. He was bitten by the gambling bug, and was now obsessed with making money. If there was a way he could acquire a few baseball cards, he could then begin trading and playing "card-pitch" to rebuild his cash coffer.

Lloyd was bitten by the gambling bug, obsessed with making money.

Word circulated to Lloyd that one of the more financially elite, Kevin, was impressed with one of his shirts, so Lloyd asked him, "How much will you give me for my western shirt?"

Kevin's answer was quick. "How 'bout five bucks?"

Lloyd knew he had him. Even at five bucks, that was more than the shirt was worth to him. "How 'bout ten?"

Kevin was taken off guard. "Nah, that's way too much!"

Lloyd said, "Well, you think about it."

Kevin was quiet through lunch and most of the afternoon that day. But Lloyd could see his repeated glances. Lloyd took the shirt out and put it on. Every time he saw Kevin looking over, he casually pulled on the collar and readjusted the cuffs.

After four hours of this, Kevin said, "I'll give you six bucks for it."

Lloyd was quick. "How 'bout nine?"

Kevin was determined. "How about $6.25?"

"No, how 'bout $9?"

"Aw, come on, Lloyd... $6.25's a good price!"

"Not for me! It's my best shirt."

Kevin stammered. Lloyd could hear him growling. "All right, how 'bout $6.50?"

Lloyd could see how this was going. "How 'bout $8.50?"

"How 'bout $7?"

Lloyd was growing tired of this, but continued. "$8.25."

Kevin's reaction was immediate. "Come on, Lloyd. You don't even wear it!"

"I don't wear it because it's my favorite shirt!"

Kevin stayed quiet for another two hours.

Lloyd thought he would just let him stew.

But Kevin was still determined to own the shirt. "I'll give you $7.25 for it!"

Lloyd was done. "$7.50's my final cut. Take it or leave it!"

There was noticeable silence emanating from the center of the ward. Then Kevin's meek voice spoke up, "All right. I'll give you $7.50 for it."

The deal was made.

Lloyd immediately called Ronnie and, through him, made a deal with a kid for fifty baseball cards, at a penny apiece. From this small stash he began a gradual monetary rebuild.

There were multiple variations of two basic baseball card-pitching games they used to compete against each other in the playroom. All mirrored the age-old "pitching pennies" game in which a group would throw pennies against a wall and the person whose penny was closest to the wall won.

One of the boy's ward versions was to require participants to pitch their card in turn against a far wall and the person whose card was closest at the end of a round, collected the pitched cards. Another version was for each individual to stand one card, each side by side, against the wall, then in turn, the person who completed knocking the last remaining card down wins. It didn't take Lloyd long to fill a shoebox full of baseball cards, replenish his "stash," and then some.

Despite the momentary pleasure of the distractions and replenishments, his impending back surgery loomed.

His impression, through years of experience with other friends, taught him that the process of correcting curvature would involve arduous months of casting the body. Plastering was the preferred therapy after surgery for most maladies at the Children's Hospital. There was an established belief that especially for children who lacked diligence, plaster casts added protection for healing. And, once set, plaster casts were seldom modified. Occasionally, windows could be cut out for persistent pressure spots if it didn't conflict with the overall integrity of the cast. Most often though, wounds developed from internal pressure were overlooked and left to heal without intervention.

For curvature corrections, patients were stretched and then plastered from above and behind the skull, under the chin, surrounding the torso, pressed hard against both hips, extending to just above each knee, exposing the arms at the armpits and front and rear windows for excrement.

The initial cast would be worn for months. Those with severe scoliosis would experience several iterations over a year until the desired spine correction was achieved.

The use of plaster of paris—a quick-setting gypsum plaster—was so extensive at the Children's Hospital that its forms were developed to a fine art. There were specific rooms set aside strictly for the purpose of casting patients. They were known as cast rooms. If not the dirtiest, the cast rooms were certainly the dustiest. Upon entering, a patient was greeted with a thick veil of white plaster dust on the floor, walls, windows, even ceiling. Tall shelves lined all four walls, stocked full of varying sizes of plaster rolls. Stacks of stainless steel basins accompanied the rolls, with two large iron sinks against the back wall with spigots from which water could be acquired to wet the plaster.

The patient was immediately transferred onto a table with a stainless steel top and steel bracing underneath. They were then stripped naked and areas to be casted were carefully wrapped in a soft, quarter-inch stretch fabric. While the various rolls of plaster were soaked, a thicker half- to one-inch cotton fabric was wrapped around the same area. After that, the rolling of the plaster began.

Being placed on a cold steel table and stretched for hours was extremely uncomfortable. A small anesthetic was usually administered, enough to help the patient relax and even sleep.

Wrapping was an "all hands on deck" procedure. It was common to have three or four people wrapping different areas at the same time. There was only a limited time within which to apply the plaster effectively. If applied too soon after soaking, it was too stiff to spread; applied too long after, and it became a gloppy, goopy pile of white-mud mess.

Wrapping was an "all hands on deck" procedure.

Often, it was a relief for patients to wake up hours later in the comfort of their own bed. Lloyd would learn that was only the beginning of his eighteen-month spine curvature correction gauntlet.

The transition to the new Ward 20 was without fanfare. One afternoon while the custodial staff transported them, Lloyd was informed that he was being moved.

Bill, in his green fatigues, said, "You're in the upper crust now."

Lloyd looked at him in question. "Whattaya mean?"

"They're moving everything of yours—lock, stock, and barrel—to the new Ward 20 upstairs. You got new digs, man!"

"Do they have all my stuff, my cabinet and all?"

"I guess so. I just do what I'm told. And we were told it's time to move you guys north."

It was smart logistical planning that the administration, Miss Laux in particular, decided to make the change while most patients were either in school or at therapy. Within a few short hours, select patients and all their belongings were moved en masse upstairs to a whole new life.

Lloyd felt pangs of the holes developing in his heart. He was smart, but not too smart. He was angry for many reasons, too many to fully comprehend. The fissures in his heart seemed endless and with each passing day, the despondency he felt missing his mother, father, sisters, and brother grew.

Through it all he remained convinced that he was invincible to whatever was thrown his way, not the least of which was the recent loss of his best friend. And the significance of parading that friend, in his shabby drug-induced state, unceremoniously through the ward was not lost on him. Clearly, it was a direct message from Miss Laux to all who would oppose her policies that you too could experience the same treatment.

It was only a matter of time before Lloyd's porous heart would finally break. But, unlike so many of his body parts, a broken heart couldn't be mended with plaster of paris.

Acknowledgments

The first person I have to thank—and believe me, "Thank" doesn't cover it—is Renate Blaschek, the only person I can clearly say is my soul-mate. There is no one I've ever met who has remained as faithful, loving, and nurturing as she. It doesn't hurt that after 43 years she's still as beautiful as the day we met. I'm looking forward to many "lives" with her.

Two people I've known who have changed my life in a positive/constructive way were the Laibows, Martin and Miriam. They met me at what could easily be called the lowest time in my life, and both jumped in with a message of hope and love over 54 years ago with only one request, "Lloyd, please, don't accept what we tell you as truth. Take it, and test if what we tell you is true for you. And, by all means, if what we've taught you in any way proves false and misleading, discard it post-hastily and with the quickest dispatch!" I continue to test everything they've imparted to me and have never found anything false or at all misleading. Their words and compassion remain a tremendous comfort to me.

I've been blessed to have three brothers and three sisters and while we've been separated due to the pandemic, I continue to love them all dearly.

Finally, I've met many wonderfully gifted people in my life I've considered "angels," people who have drifted in and out of my life and, have proven to be an invaluable asset to me and Renate. While I continue to hold you all dearly, there is not enough space here to thank you all adequately. Please know that you are loved, because I love you.

Made in the USA
Middletown, DE
03 October 2023

40081452R00126